CW00864746

Two Weeks with the Queen

A play by Mary Morris

Based on the novel by Morris Gleitzman

PEARSON
Longman

Pearson Education Limited
Edinburgh Gate
Harlow
Essex
CM20 2JE
England
and Associated Companies throughout the World

First published 1993 by Currency Press Ltd

This educational edition first published by Pearson Education 2007
10 9

Activities by Emma Lee

Cover image © Stockbyte / Corbis

ISBN: 978-1-4058-5682-9

Printed in China
EPC/09

Contents

Characters and setting   v

Act One   1

Act Two   43

Activities   90

Characters

COLIN MUDFORD	*a twelve-year-old boy*
LUKE	*Colin's younger brother*
MUM	
DAD	
AUNTIE IRIS	*Colin's aunt in England*
UNCLE BOB	*Colin's uncle in England*
ALISTAIR	*Colin's cousin in England*
GRIFF	*an AIDS patient in hospital*
TED	*Griff's partner*

The play is usually performed by six actors using character doubling for the extra roles.

BUSINESSMAN	NURSE
GUARD	MATRON
AMERICAN TOURIST	FLIGHT ATTENDANT
SPANISH TOURIST	CAPTAIN
PATIENT	POLICEMAN
AIRPORT CHECK-IN STAFF	ENGLISH NURSE
CAFE STAFF	ENGLISH DOCTOR
DOCTOR 1	ENGLISH STUDENT DOCTORS
DOCTOR 2	DR GRAHAM

Setting

The Mudfords' home; hospital in Australia and London; the home of Colin's relations in London; outside Buckingham Palace; inside Ted's flat; on a plane and at the airport in Sydney and London.

Act One Scene One

The music of God Save the Queen *is heard, followed by the plummy voice of Her Majesty delivering her Christmas message.*

At the Mudfords' place Mum *and* Dad, *barefoot and dressed in shorts, singlets and paper hats, are fanning themselves with a bit torn off a beer carton. They are watching the Queen's Christmas message on TV.* Colin, *also in shorts and very scuffed brown elastic-sided boots, sits some way from them glaring at an open shoe box containing a pair of sensible black school shoes. His kid brother* Luke *runs in and out strafing everybody and everything with his new MiG fighter plane.* Colin *picks up a shoe and looks at it with distaste.*

Queen	And a very merry Christmas to you all.
Colin	Merry flamin' Christmas. (Luke *strafes him.*) Gerroff!
Luke	Wanna go?
Colin	Get lost.

Luke *does a circle of the room shooting down the enemy and swoops on* Colin *again.* Colin *throws a shoe at him.*

Luke	He hit me! Dad, he hit me!
Dad	Don't hit your brother, Colin.
Colin	I didn't…
Mum	You heard your father.
Colin	It was him, he started…
Dad	That's enough! We're trying to listen to the Queen here.

1

COLIN	Nobody ever listens to me.
LUKE	That's cos you're not the Queen.
DAD	Just keep it down to a roar, eh?

DAD snuggles MUM closer to him and they settle back with the Queen who rabbits on about equality and justice for all.

COLIN	(*quietly, in Luke's direction*) Lucky for you I'm not the Queen. If I was I'd have you locked in the tower and torture you and put you on the rack till your bones creak and then I'd have your fingernails pulled out one by one and then I'd pour boiling oil on you and hang you from the battlements and then I'd…
LUKE	Mum, I don't feel well.
COLIN	Then I'd have you cut open right down the middle and your guts would hang out and all the blow flies would come and the crows would peck out your eyes…
LUKE	(*louder*) Mum, I feel sick.
MUM	Serves you right for having four serves of chrissie pud.
COLIN	Four?! I only got three!
LUKE	I do, but. (*He goes back to playing with his MiG.*)
COLIN	Prob'ly a strain of heat resistant bacteria in the chrissie pud. If I'd got a *microscope* for Christmas instead of a pair of school shoes I could have run some tests and spotted it. We'll prob'ly all come down with it now.
DAD	Colin, go and shut the back door mate – keep some of the heat out.
COLIN	Why can't he go?
DAD	Cos I asked you to.
COLIN	Yeh, well he'd be quicker, he's got turbo thrusters, I've only got lace-ups.

*M*UM *and* D*AD* *exchange a guilty glance.*

MUM   Luke, go and shut the door. (L*UKE* *goes*, D*AD* *turns the*
          Queen off.) Love, about the microscope…

DAD   Next time, eh?

MUM   We just couldn't stretch to it.

COLIN   I know, the recession.

MUM   Besides, you needed shoes.

COLIN   (*looking at his appalling boots*) No I didn't.

DAD   (*picking up a shoe*) They're pretty snazzy shoes. Bloke
          could end up Prime Minister in shoes like those.

MUM   They are the ones you liked in the shop – aren't they?

COLIN   Yes, they're, um, they're good.

MUM   Colin love, is there something else bothering you?

COLIN   (*shrugging*) Nuh.

DAD   You can talk to us mate, you know that.

COLIN   Well…

MUM   Yes love?

COLIN   It's just that… well…

DAD   Yes?

COLIN   Nobody ever…

LUKE   (*entering the room*) Mum. Mum!

As they turn towards L*UKE*, *he collapses on the floor.* M*UM* *and*
D*AD* *rush towards him.*

COLIN   Pays any attention to me.

The sound of an ambulance is heard.

At the hospital MUM *and* DAD *are waiting anxiously for news.* COLIN *is fidgeting. There is a table nearby, laden with medical bits and pieces including a microscope.*

COLIN	Why wouldn't the ambulance driver let me in the ambulance? Eh? I never been in an ambulance. Why wouldn't she?
MUM	(*absently*) Mmmmmm?
COLIN	Not as if there wasn't any room.
DAD	Just leave it, son.
COLIN	No Christmas spirit, I reckon.

A DOCTOR *enters.*

DOCTOR 1	Mr and Mrs Mudford?
MUM AND DAD	How is he? Is he alright?
DOCTOR 1	Don't worry, it doesn't look too serious, probably just the excitement of the season.
COLIN	(*to* DOCTOR) I reckon it's gastric.
DOCTOR 1	Gastric, eh?
COLIN	If it's any help I can tell you what he's eaten today: one bowl of Coco-pops; three jelly snakes; some Licorice Allsorts; a packet of Minties; six gherkins; half a giant pack of Twisties and five chocolate Santas. Then for lunch…
DOCTOR 1	Enough already!

COLIN	You can faint from overeating, I've done it with jelly snakes. You see, the large intestine blocks the flow of blood to the brain…
DOCTOR 1	Thanks for the tip.
COLIN	Maybe an enema would help, or a very large dose of castor oil…

DAD *grabs* COLIN *and under the guise of putting an arm round him, clamps his mouth.*

MUM	You're sure it's nothing serious?
DOCTOR 1	We've taken a few blood tests and sent them off to Sydney, results will be back in a couple of days. We'll know more then.
MUM	A couple of days!
DAD	There's no way of doing them sooner?
DOCTOR 1	The top people don't live out here, unfortunately.
MUM	But you said it wasn't serious.
DOCTOR 1	It's just a precaution. I'm sure you'll have him home 1 in a couple of days.
DAD	The Doc knows what he's talking about, love. Couple of days and he'll be falling out of trees with the best of them.
MUM	Ray! Not in front of the doctor!
DAD	Alright, um… Catching snakes with the best of them?

MUM *rolls her eyes.*

COLIN	Playing cricket.
DAD	Yes, that's it. Playing cricket. (*He winks at* COLIN.)
DOCTOR 1	I'm sure you're right. If you'd like to pop into the office, we'll get a few details.

MUM	(*to* COLIN) You wait here love. We won't be long.
COLIN	But I could have important medical information…
DAD	Stay!

COLIN *stays. The others leave. He discovers the microscope then goes out and returns pushing the trolley upon which* LUKE *lies.*

LUKE	Put me back, I'll tell Mum, put me back.
COLIN	Here, give us your arm.
LUKE	What for?
COLIN	I told ya. I just want a little bit of blood to put under the microscope.
LUKE	No.
COLIN	Come on, it won't hurt. (**He takes out his Swiss army knife.**)
LUKE	Help! Mum! Dad! Help!
COLIN	Shut up willya. Look, if you could see how worried they are having to wait for Sydney to do the tests. Just give me a little bit of blood, I can check it out for germs and put their minds at rest.
LUKE	I don't want to.
COLIN	How could you be so selfish – at Christmas too?
LUKE	Don't care.
COLIN	But it's for Mum and Dad.
LUKE	I gave them place mats.
COLIN	Okay. Forget it.
LUKE	Put me back now?

COLIN	Yeh, alright. Hey, I just had an idea. You know when you fell in the creek and scraped your elbow on the old ute chassis that was in there?
LUKE	Yeh.
COLIN	You could have got metal poisoning.
LUKE	But it's nearly better.
COLIN	Yeh, but infection could have got in. Better let me have a look at the scab.
LUKE	You reckon?

LUKE *twists the elbow to look.* COLIN *looks too. He suddenly picks the scab off.*

LUKE	OW! What you do that for!
COLIN	I told you, I just want to check for wriggly things.

COLIN *dabs at the elbow with a hanky and gets to work at the microscope.*

LUKE	I'm gunna tell on you.
COLIN	At school we looked in this dead frog through the microscope and there was all these wriggly things and Mr Blair our biology teacher reckoned they were germs.
LUKE	That was my best scab.
COLIN	(*still looking*) Hey there aren't any. You're a faker. There's nuthin' wrong with you. Not a single germ.
LUKE	Are you sure?
COLIN	Not a single wriggle.
LUKE	Maybe people's blood doesn't wriggle like frogs'.
COLIN	It's not the blood that wriggles, it's the germs. Your blood is as healthy as mine.

LUKE	How do you know? You haven't tested yours.
COLIN	I just know.
LUKE	You have to test it otherwise it's not scientific.
COLIN	Alright, alright. (*He takes out his knife and with great trepidation prepares to cut himself.*)
LUKE	No! Not with that. I got a safety pin in my underdaks. (*He fumbles under the covers.*) Here.

COLIN *pricks himself with the pin and puts a spot of blood on the hanky. He puts it under the microscope.*

	Well?
COLIN	Oh no!
LUKE	What?
COLIN	Wriggly things. Omigod. I've got it.
LUKE	Got what?
COLIN	I dunno do I? Something worse than you've got. I'm gonna die. Get me a doctor quick.
LUKE	Doctor nothin'. If they find out what we're doin' you'll get killed anyway. Put me back.

A NURSE *arrives and sees* LUKE.

NURSE	You been to X-Ray and back already, love? I don't know what's up with these orderlies leaving you out here. Too much of a hurry to get their Christmas pud inside them eh?

COLIN *groans, but the* NURSE *ignores him and takes* LUKE *back to the ward.* COLIN *staggers about moaning. A* DOCTOR *enters wearing a red plastic nose and a party hat. He is jingling his car keys and singing a Christmas song.*

COLIN	'Scuse me. You a doctor?

DOCTOR 2	Sort of. But I'm finished for the day. Roast turkey, here I come. (COLIN *groans*.) You okay mate?
COLIN	I reckon I got gastric. Or worse.
DOCTOR 2	You reckon?
COLIN	Yep. I just tested my blood. Maybe you could give me a second opinion.
DOCTOR 2	Sure. Let's have a look. Hold these a minute.

The DOCTOR *looks at the hanky through the microscope.* COLIN *checks out the car keys. They have a Mercedes symbol attached.* COLIN *is impressed.*

	Um, has this hanky been in contact with a dead animal by any chance?
COLIN	Only a frog. I wrapped the frog in it after biology when I took it home in my lunch box.
DOCTOR 2	Sorry I asked.
COLIN	Can you see the germs?
DOCTOR 2	Yep. But they're not yours, they're the frog's. You, by the look of you, are as fit as a bullock.
COLIN	Well, how come when I put my brother's blood under there on the same hanky there was no germs?
DOCTOR 2	That bit of the hanky must have stayed clean, by some miracle.
COLIN	(*disappointed*) You mean I'm not gonna die?
DOCTOR 2	Not for a bit. Hey are you with that boy who came in earlier, um, Luke Mudford?
COLIN	My kid brother.
DOCTOR 2	Bit of a pain, eh? Bloke gets a bit ignored when his kid brother's in hospital.

COLIN   You're not wrong. These really the keys for your car?

DOCTOR 2   Yep.

COLIN   Phew, radical.

DOCTOR 2   Look, don't worry about your brother. He'll be home in a couple of days.

COLIN   Prob'ly.

DOCTOR 2   Trust me. (*He retrieves his keys.*) You don't get a car like this by being wrong. (*He goes.*)

COLIN   Yeah. Radical.

Mum is yelling down the phone to Iris in England.

MUM
Yes … Yes … No, he's fine. They've taken a blood sample … Tomorrow. We get the results tomorrow … Yes … Ambulance, that's right … No … No, completely out of the blue. One minute he was fine, next he was on the floor ... The floor … The FLOOR... No, he had his Christmas dinner … Yes … Yes it is hot over here. I expect it's cold over there in Pommy-land … Snow? Oh, nice … Yes … Yes we'll let you know. Love to Bob and little Alistair … Yes … Bye … Bye Iris … Yes … Bye love … Yes, you too. Bye.

Mum leaves.

In the hospital ward Luke, *dressed in a hospital gown, gets
set to bat. A* Nurse *sets a pile of bedpans for a wicket and
gets down to catch.* Colin *enters running from off and bowls
a beauty.* Luke *hits it off for six. From out of sight a loud
matronly voice yells 'howzat!'* Matron *enters holding the ball
between finger and thumb, her face sour.*

Nurse	Shit!

The Nurse *bundles* Luke *back into bed.*

Colin	It's alright, it's a soft ball. We're allowed to play with it indoors at home.
Matron	(*to the* Nurse) Most irresponsible behaviour. This is a hospital, not the SCG. That child is very sick.
Nurse	Matron, the patient wasn't involved…

The bat falls out of Luke's *bed.*

Matron	This will go on your report…
Colin	You won't sack her willya? It wasn't her fault, besides a bit of cricket never hurt anyone…

Matron *fixes him with a look that would stop a train and he
retreats.* Dad *enters and the* Matron *talks quietly to him and
then goes.* Dad *hovers over* Luke, *whispering earnestly and
patting him awkwardly, while* Colin *composes a letter to* Matron.

Dear Matron. Overseas, where they have the best
hospitals in the world, cricket is often used to help
patients get better. Spin bowling is good exercise for
people who've done their wrists in, and batting is
specially good for gastric because it strengthens the
bowel muscles…

DAD *approaches* COLIN *looking very serious.*

Oh-oh. I'm in it now. Em, did you see Luke's six, Dad? Reckon he must be almost better, eh?

DAD Col, the hospital in Sydney that did tests on Luke's blood want to do some more. He has to go down there, today.

COLIN Sydney! Far out. Are we all going down in the car?

DAD That'd take too long. They're going to fly him down in the air ambulance this afternoon.

COLIN A plane?! We're going to Sydney on a plane? WOW!

DAD There's only room for one passenger so I'm going with him. You and Mum'll come down on the train tomorrow.

COLIN Aw no! Da-ad!

DAD *mistakes* COLIN*'s disappointment for worry about* LUKE.

DAD I know it's a shock old mate. I'm worried sick myself. Um, you wanna say goodbye to your brother?

COLIN See ya Luke.

LUKE See ya Col.

The NURSE *wheels* LUKE *out.*

DAD Your Mum's a bit upset about it all, so I want you to look after her for me. Promise? (COLIN *nods.*) We got to be tough. Alright, mate?

DAD *follows* LUKE *out. The* NURSE *re-enters and solemnly picks up the bedpans and the cricket gear. She looks at* COLIN *and smiles.*

NURSE It was a great six, but.

At home, MUM *paces up and down.* COLIN *enters the room carrying a plate and a fork.*

COLIN	Sit down. Your tea's ready.

She sits. He watches anxiously as she pokes the fork into the meal.

MUM	It looks lovely. What is it?
COLIN	Curry.
MUM	Why is it green?
COLIN	It's pea curry.
MUM	Oh. (*She puts a bit in her mouth and chews.*)
COLIN	Is it good?
MUM	Very nice, love. Um, I like the glacé cherries.
COLIN	It's a sweet curry.

MUM *puts some more in her mouth. Her face crumples and she fights back sobs.*

Oh no. I didn't get all the lumps of curry powder out. I'll get you a drink of water.

He runs off. MUM *composes herself.* COLIN *returns and presses a glass of water in her hand.*

MUM	Colin. There's something we haven't made clear to you about Luke.
COLIN	Your curry's getting cold.
MUM	The reason they've sent him to Sydney is because they think he might be pretty crook.

COLIN	Mum, stop worrying. You've seen those Sydney hospitals on telly; they got everything. They could cure a horse with its head on backwards down there. Come on, eat your curry.
MUM	Good on you Col.
COLIN	'Member that show they had on every week about operations and stuff? That was from Sydney. 'Member the kid who swallowed her Dad's record player – not all at once, just bits of it and you could see all the bits on the X-ray and then they opened her up and found all the things her Mum and Dad had been lookin' for all year? Then there was that man whose heart went bung and they put a new one in, and the surgeon had it in his hand all bloody an beatin' all by itself – and remember the bloke who cut his foot off with the lawnmower and had it sewn back on? You're not eatin' your tea.
MUM	Sorry love, I'm not very hungry. Tired I expect.
COLIN	Put your feet up for a bit if you like.
MUM	Yeh, I might do that.

MUM *puts her feet up and* COLIN *picks up the plate of curry.*

COLIN	I'll put this in the fridge. You might feel like it for breakfast.

MUM *smiles weakly.* COLIN *takes the plate away. He returns and covers* MUM *with a rug. She sniffs and tries to be brave.* COLIN *lifts the rug and gets in beside her. He slips one arm under her neck and she snuggles against him. He wraps the rug round them both and hugs her tight. They turn the lights out. In the dark the phone rings and then stops.*

*Mum is carrying a bundle of Colin-size clothes. She starts
folding them into a huge suitcase. Colin enters yawning.*

COLIN	Morning Mum. Gor, you sure you're packin enough? They've probly got a kitchen sink in Sydney, you know.
MUM	This is not for Sydney.
COLIN	But them's my clothes.
MUM	Colin, your Dad rung from the Sydney hospital last night. Him and me… We'd like you to go and stay with Uncle Bob and Auntie Iris in England for a bit.
COLIN	Wha… ?
MUM	We're not going to make you go. But we'd like you to. For your sake and for ours.
COLIN	I can't go to England – cricket practice starts next week.
MUM	You'll have a great time over there. Uncle Bob and Auntie Iris live near London Zoo and Uncle Bob goes to the cricket all the time. And little Alistair, your cousin, he's practically your age.
COLIN	What'd I do…?
MUM	Oh love, it's not that. It's just for the best. The doctors say Luke isn't going to get better.
COLIN	From gastric? People always get better from gastric!
MUM	It's not gastric. They showed Dad the X-rays. It's… It's…
COLIN	No! I can be a help to you! I can make the tea so you can look after him. I can bring him his homework from school. You don't have to send me away!

MUM	Colin, a terrible thing's happening and we don't want you to have to suffer too.
COLIN	What terrible thing? What's so terrible you have to send me away?
MUM	Don't you understand! Luke's got cancer! He's going to die!

She rushes out. COLIN *shouts after her.*

COLIN	Bull! I don't believe you! They're bein' slack! If they can sew a bloke's foot on and put a new heart in somebody surely they can cure a bit of cancer! (*He starts to throw his clothes angrily out of the suitcase.*) What about the man in the newsagents? He had cancer on his head and they cured him. Expect me to believe that you can get the cricket from India and get bombs that could blow the whole world up and robots and space ships and they can't cure a bit of cancer! Bull! They're just not tryin'! (*He slumps down.*) Bloody slack. If it was somebody important they'd pull their finger out alright. If it was the Prime Minister they'd be askin' the Queen of England for the world's best doctor's phone number then, eh? I bet the Queen has the world's best doctor right there beside her in London. London! (*He starts throwing the clothes back in the suitcase. He picks it up and leaves the room.*) Hey Mum. What time's my plane?

COLIN, MUM and DAD are waiting at the airport for the plane to board.

COLIN	You don't have to worry. Everything's going to be OK.
DAD	Good on ya, Col.
COLIN	No, I mean, Luke isn't going to die.
DAD	Don't son.
COLIN	Mum, are you listening? I said, Luke isn't going to die.
MUM	(*sharply*) Don't talk about things you don't understand.
COLIN	I do understand.
DAD	Colin, it's not up to us.
COLIN	I know. That's what I'm trying to explain.
MUM	(*too brightly*) Why don't you think about all the exciting things you're going to do with Uncle Bob and Auntie Iris and Alistair.
COLIN	Stack me, some people don't want to be cheered up! Mum, I'm trying to tell you about Luke.
MUM	Don't talk about it. Please don't.

DAD takes him aside while MUM composes herself.

DAD	We've got to be strong old mate, and cop it on the chin.
COLIN	But Dad...
DAD	Now, when you write to Luke, don't say anything about... You know.

COLIN	The cancer.
DAD	The doctors haven't and we've decided not to. Don't want him scared on top of everything.
COLIN	Don't worry, I won't say anything about him dying, cos he's not going to.
MUM	(*joining them again*) Be a good boy for Uncle Bob and Auntie Iris, won't you? It was kind of them to help out with the ticket and everything.
COLIN	Yeh, yeh.

A FLIGHT ATTENDANT *approaches.*

FLIGHT ATT	Colin Mudford?
MUM	Yes, this is Colin.
FLIGHT ATT	I'm your flight attendant. I'll be looking after you on the plane.
COLIN	Let's go.
FLIGHT ATT	We'll get you boarded then.
MUM	Oh, your passport – here, and some English money. It's not much, but…
COLIN	I won't need much.
MUM	It's for the best, love. We'll send for you soon – once it's all… When it's all…
DAD	We'll leave you to it then, son.
FLIGHT ATT	Don't worry, we'll see him right.
MUM	And keep warm, won't you?

COLIN *embraces* MUM.

COLIN	(*to* DAD) Don't worry, I got it all worked out. I got a plan.

LOUDSPEAKER **VOICE**	This is your boarding call for Qantas flight number one to London via Melbourne and Singapore. Now boarding at gate ten, Qantas flight number one to London via Melbourne and Singapore.

The ATTENDANT *takes* COLIN *to his seat.*

FLIGHT ATT   This is your call button. If you need a drink or anything, just press it. Someone will come round with headphones and there'll be a movie later.

COLIN   This is great. How long is it?

FLIGHT ATT   Oh, twenty-four hours or so.

COLIN   No, the plane, not the flight.

FLIGHT ATT   Oh, sorry. (*She tells him in metres.*)

COLIN   You know, that's long enough for an indoor cricket pitch. If you moved all the seats out down one side you could have one, then all your passengers would get the exercise which would counteract the effects of jet lag.

FLIGHT ATT   I'll pass that on to the Captain.

A grim-faced BUSINESSMAN *rushes in late and sits beside* COLIN. *The* ATTENDANT *goes through the usual vacuous safety routine to the unintelligible voice on the intercom. The noise of the plane taxi-ing for take-off is heard. Throughout the flight, the* BUSINESSMAN *tries to ignore* COLIN.

COLIN   (*to the* BUSINESSMAN) Lifejackets! Great. You think we better get ours out? You'd be right. In the water, I mean. Got enough fat on you to keep you warm. I'd be a gonner. (*The noise rises in pitch.*) Woa, some speed eh? Did you know most plane crashes happen on take-off? (*They lean back as the plane takes off.*) Hey, there's Sydney harbour bridge. Isn't it beautiful? My brother's in Sydney, in hospital. You reckon they're all lookin' up at us while we're lookin' down? I bet him and all the Nurses are lookin' out the hospital window at us. Wave, go on, just in case. I bet he's ropable, he only got to go in the air ambulance, I'm in a jumbo. Boo sucks Lukey mate!

Later.

Gor, they don't half feed you a lot. I'm as stuffed as a Christmas turkey.

The BUSINESSMAN *gives a grunt of pain.*

Is that a bit of cancer?

BUSINESSMAN	I beg your pardon?
COLIN	Cancer. It's where the cells start growing too fast inside your body and your whole system can go bung. I've been reading up on it.
BUSINESSMAN	I know what it is. I just don't particularly want to talk about it.
COLIN	Funny that. My folks are the same. Why not?
BUSINESSMAN	Because it's not a very pleasant topic.
COLIN	There's worse topics. (*He thinks.*) Like nuclear war and why sick has carrots in it. (*The* BUSINESSMAN *groans.*) Only, if you've got it, I'd have it seen to.
BUSINESSMAN	I haven't got it! I've got indigestion.
COLIN	Mum always gets indigestion if she bolts her tucker.

Later.

You want a go at doing this quiz? Which Prime Minister played cricket for Australia? No? Do you want to colour in this picture of a Koala? The crayons are a bit crappy but it was good of the Hostie to give it to me.

The CAPTAIN *and the* ATTENDANT *appear.*

CAPTAIN   G'day Colin. Thought you might like a look at the flight deck.

COLIN   Too right! (*He stands.*)

BUSINESSMAN Excuse me miss, do you have any other seats available?

COLIN   Oh, don't worry. I'm going up to the flight deck, so you can have both seats for a while.

CAPTAIN   So. We're travelling to London by ourselves, eh?

COLIN   Well, I am.

CAPTAIN   And what are you going to do in London?

COLIN   I'm going to see the Queen.

CAPTAIN   The Queen, eh? (*He winks at the* ATTENDANT.) Going to drop in for tea and cucumber sandwiches are you?

COLIN   No. I'm going to ask her to help cure my brother's cancer.

CAPTAIN   Ar, em, yes, well...

       Later.

COLIN   (*returning to his seat*) You should see the equipment and all the dials and lights and everything. Here we are, in a plane bigger than Myers up in the air sixty thousand feet over Dubrovnik; if modern technology can do this, it can cure cancer standing on its head. What do you reckon?

       Later.

             And then Arnie Strachan told me that when his uncle died they put his ashes in a box and sent them to his rellies in England. Only, they put him in the same parcel as things to put in the Christmas cake, so the rellies thought his uncle's ashes was some new kind of spices and they put him in the Christmas cake, cos they sent the letter separate, see, and the letter didn't get there until after the cake was made. And the letter said that his uncle wanted to be buried at sea, so they took the cake out on the ferry and chucked bits of it in the water, only these seagulls kept swooping and carrying bits of him off. Anyway...

Later. COLIN *is sound asleep.*

FLIGHT ATT   Ladies and gentlemen. We hope you had a pleasant flight. The temperature at Heathrow is minus two degrees, and the time is five fifteen p.m. Please remain in your seats until the aircraft has taxied to a complete halt. We ask that you take care when opening overhead lockers as luggage may fall out and cause injury. Exit will be through the forward door only. Thank you for choosing to fly Qantas. We hope we can be of service to you again when next you travel.

The BUSINESSMAN *leaves looking like death. The* ATTENDANT *wakes* COLIN *and takes him off the plane.*

COLIN *yawns and stretches, looks around and shivers. The* ATTENDANT *returns with his suitcase and a notice on a stick with his name in large letters.*

FLIGHT ATT	Just wait here for them. They can't miss you.
COLIN	What if they don't come?
FLIGHT ATT	They will.
COLIN	But what if they don't?
FLIGHT ATT	(*winking*) Then I'll take you home with me, eh?
COLIN	I wouldn't mind.
FLIGHT ATT	Watch it! Anyway, I'll come back and check in five minutes, just in case. See ya, Colin Mudford. (*She goes.*)
COLIN	See ya. (*He waits.*) Wonder what they're like? I hope they're understanding types. (*He practises telling them.*) Nice to meet you Uncle Bob and Auntie Iris, but I've really come to London to meet the Queen. (*He answers himself as* UNCLE BOB.) Oh, is that right young man? Well, if our 'ot dinners and spare bed aren't good enough for you, you can rack off!

BOB, IRIS *and* ALISTAIR *arrive.*

IRIS	I told you we'd be late. Stop sniffing Alistair. (ALISTAIR *sniffs.*)
BOB	You heard your mother.
IRIS	We should have parked in the airport car park.
BOB	I'm not parking in that car park.

Iris	Alistair, where's your hanky?
Bob	The way they charge to park a car.
Iris	Well, we're late now, you and your car park.
Bob	They're not getting it out of me. I can tell you that much.
Iris	There he is! Hello Colin love.

There are hello's and handshakes and kisses all round.

	Well. Just look at you. How's your Mum?
Colin	She's good.
Iris	And your Dad?
Colin	Good.
Iris	Alistair don't stand like that, love. It's bad for your spine.
Colin	Luke's a bit crook, but.
Iris	Um, yes, well. Alistair!
Alistair	Sorry.
Bob	I'm not paying for you to have your posture straightened.
Iris	Well! Shall we be off then?
Colin	Just a tick.

Colin opens his suitcase and pulls out a jumper. He puts it on. Then he pulls out several more and puts them on.

Right.

They leave.

COLIN is being shown the spare bed in ALISTAIR's bedroom.

IRIS	This is your bed. I hope you'll be comfortable, love. You'll soon get 'climatised. Don't pick your scalp Alistair.
BOB	I expect you'll be wanting to see the sights, soon as you've got over your jet lag.
ALISTAIR	The Zoo's good.
IRIS	Big Ben. Alistair!
BOB	You heard your mother. You'll get scabs, you will.
COLIN	I want to go to Buckingham Palace.
BOB	What would you want to go to that dump for?
IRIS	Er … now what else is there…?
BOB	Waste of taxpayer's money, that place. Ought to be pulled down.
IRIS	Madame Tussaud's?
COLIN	Well, not the palace really. It's the Queen I want to see.
ALISTAIR	Oh-oh.
BOB	Don't you talk to me about the Queen!
IRIS	Alright Bob…
BOB	Get me started on the Queen…
IRIS	Don't mind Uncle Bob, love. He's got a bit of a thing about, you know, them.
ALISTAIR	Thinks they should be stuffed and put in a museum.

IRIS	Alright thank you, Alistair. (*to* COLIN) We don't go into the city much, as a rule. But don't worry, Alistair here will show you all the sights, won't you love?
ALISTAIR	Will I?
IRIS	Go on love, show him.
ALISTAIR	Huh?
IRIS	Get it out and show him.
ALISTAIR	Oh, yeh. (*He gets out a picture book.*)
IRIS	Got everything in there. London Bridge, Hyde Park. Lovely colours.
ALISTAIR	And the Royal family.
BOB	Talk to me about the bloomin' Queen...
IRIS	We'll have a bit of an outing tomorrow, if it's nice.
BOB	Good idea.
IRIS	Do you good. Take your mind off... the flight and...
BOB	Things.
COLIN	Great.
BOB	Tell you what. Tomorrow after work, we'll take you to the biggest do-it-yourself hardware centre in Greater London.
COLIN	Great.
BOB	We were a bit worried when they first built it, but it's the focal point of the district now.
IRIS	Yes, we're very pleased with it. Do you know, it's bigger than Fulham football ground.
COLIN	Mmmmm.

BOB	Got everything in there for the home improvements. Nothing's too small or too big. And videos running to show you how to do things, like.

COLIN *yawns.*

IRIS	Oh look, he's tired. We'll let you have an early night love, eh?
COLIN	No, it's not that. It's just that I'm finding it a bit hard to concentrate on hardware at the moment while Luke's got cancer.
IRIS	Yes, um, well I think an early night for all of us. Leave that alone, Alistair.
ALISTAIR	I wasn't…
BOB	You heard your mother.
IRIS	We won't wake you in the morning love. Let you have a lie in. Alistair's coming to work with me tomorrow so I can take him to the doctor's.
ALISTAIR	I'm sickening for something.
BOB	You make yourself right at home tomorrow.
IRIS	There's the telly and the radio and Uncle Bob's do-it-yourself magazines…
BOB	The important thing is to relax and take your mind completely off, you know… things.
COLIN	Thanks.
IRIS	Nighty-night then. Don't forget your teeth, Alistair.

They start to leave, whispering.

	Did you hear him? He said it right out. Couldn't believe my ears.
BOB	He's a bit of a funny one alright.

IRIS	Right out loud…

They go.

ALISTAIR *gets undressed and puts his pj's on.*

ALISTAIR	You nearly got him started on the Queen.
COLIN	What's he got against her?
ALISTAIR	I don't know. Something about how she never had to get her hands dirty.
COLIN	Well, she wouldn't would she? She's the Queen.
ALISTAIR	Yeh.
COLIN	Where exactly is Buckingham Palace?
ALISTAIR	In town. Miles away.
COLIN	How do you get there?
ALISTAIR	Quickest way's by tube, but it's pretty dangerous. You have to get in the same carriage as dozens of other people. You can catch cold, or flu, or anything. Well, not anything. A lot of things, but not, you know, anything.
COLIN	Its OK Alistair. I know you don't catch cancer from other people.
ALISTAIR	Mum said that word wasn't to be mentioned in this house.
COLIN	What word?
ALISTAIR	That word.
COLIN	Cancer?
ALISTAIR	Shooosh!
IRIS	(*from out of sight*) Lights out boys.

ALISTAIR   Aren't you going to put your pyjamas on?

COLIN   Um, what's the temperature get down to round here?

ALISTAIR   Don't know. Never took much notice.

COLIN looks at his pj's, takes off one jumper and puts the pj's on top of his clothes.

COLIN   Night then.

ALISTAIR   Er... Yeh.

People are rushing about in noisy London. Their clothing reflects the multi-cultural and business nature of the city. COLIN enters bewildered and wide eyed.

COLIN   'Scuse me …'Scuse … Could you tell me which train goes to Buckingham Palace. 'Scuse me?

Everybody ignores him. He rushes about trying to get someone to answer him. Finally the crowd mills around him in an organic mass. COLIN cannot escape. The mass takes him on a tube. They rattle along hanging on to straps.

Could you tell me please where to get off for Buckingham Palace? 'Scuse me.

COLIN struggles to get a map out and tries to read it to no avail. Suddenly the crowd lurches as the tube stops and the mass carries COLIN off the tube. Then they all scatter in different directions. COLIN is alone. A huge set of wrought iron gates appears. He does not see them and yells out.

Would someone please tell me how to get to Buckingham Palace!!!! (*He notices the gates.*) Oh. Right. Good one.

As Colin *peers through the gates, a guard in red tunic and tall bearskin hat appears. The* Guard *spends most of the next few minutes repressing an intense desire to laugh.*

Colin	G'day. (*The guard does not respond.*) Geez, they're a friendly mob round here. 'Scuse me. I'm here to see the Queen?

A tourist or two wander up.

American Tourist	Hey, kid. You're in my picture.
Colin	(*to guard*) Please tell the Queen that Colin Mudford is here from Australia.
Spanish Tourist	(*grinning*) And Manuel Corbes from Madrid.
Colin	I need her Majesty's help. Hello? (*No response*) Maybe it's my accent. (*He tries to sound posh.*) It is an urgent medical matter. My... brother... Luke... has... got... a... serious... medical... condition.

The Guard *twitches.*

American	That don't give you the right to mess up other people's photo opportunities.
Colin	Just let me in and I'll explain inside.
Spaniard	Me too.
Colin	Look. I know you're probably not meant to open the gate and you probably get people lying through their teeth all the time, but I promise you I'm telling the truth and if you open the gate I'll explain everything to

the Queen and you won't lose your job or get sent to
Northern Ireland.

The GUARD *nearly loses control. A* POLICEMAN *enters behind*
COLIN, *who loses his temper.*

You'd better open that gate, cos when the Queen finds
out you've kept a sick kid waiting, she's gunna do you!

The POLICEMAN *collars* COLIN.

POLICEMAN	Now then, son. What seems to be the problem?
COLIN	At last. Well, I need to see the Queen.
POLICEMAN	You do, do you?
COLIN	Yes. And I reckon this bloke's a bit deaf or… you know (*He makes loony gestures.*)… something. So if you could just unlock the gate for me.
POLICEMAN	Unlock the gate.
COLIN	Yes, thanks.
POLICEMAN	(*laughing*) That's a good one. Unlock the gate, eh?
COLIN	If you wouldn't mind. I need to see the Queen about my sick brother.
SPANIARD	And my sick mother.
POLICEMAN	Do yourself a favour, and write her a letter about it, cos if I see you hanging around here again, you'll be the one who's feeling sick. (*He roars.*) Gotit!? Now push off. (COLIN *pushes off.*) Who does he think he is? Kylie Bleedin' Minogue?
SPANIARD	Qué?

A squeak escapes from the GUARD. *The* POLICEMAN *turns to
check him out. The* GUARD *is stoney-faced.*

34

COLIN *reads from the letter he has just written.*

COLIN   Dear your Majesty the Queen. I need to speak to you
             urgently about my brother Luke. He's got cancer and
             the doctors in Australia are being really slack. If I could
             borrow your top doctor for a while I know he/she
             would fix things up in no time. Of course Mum and
             Dad would pay his/her fares even if it meant selling the
             car or getting a loan. Please contact me at the above
             address urgently. Yours sincerely, Colin Mudford. PS.
             This is not a hoax. Ring the above number and Auntie
             Iris will tell you. Hang up if a man answers. (*He puts
             it in an envelope and looks at it.*) Two days, I reckon.
             Three tops.

Act One Scene Fourteen

Iris and Bob are putting coats and scarves on, getting ready to go to work.

IRIS	Now Alistair, take two kelp tablets every four hours with water and one vitamin C tablet every two hours with milk and no running around. Ooh, is that the post?
ALISTAIR	I'll get it.

Colin flies past him, returns with it and leafs anxiously through the letters.

IRIS	Don't fret love. You've only been here a week, it takes at least that for a letter to come from Australia.
BOB	Don't talk to me about letters.
IRIS	Bit homesick, are you pet?
BOB	What about that Christmas card? Came from Cheshire via Israel.
IRIS	You can give Mum and Dad a quick ring if you like, just the once.
COLIN	No, it's OK, I'm fine. Thanks anyway.
IRIS	Now, stay indoors with your chest Alistair. Lunch is in the fridge. Bye loves.
BOB	You heard your mother. Ta-ta then. (*They go.*)
ALISTAIR	Colin?
COLIN	What?
ALISTAIR	Have you really ridden a trail bike, or were you pulling my leg?

COLIN	Straight up. Yamaha 250. Twin exhaust, cross-country gear ratios.
ALISTAIR	Brill.
COLIN	Yeh, it was alright till the brakes failed and I went over the cliff.
ALISTAIR	You went over a cliff?
COLIN	Yeh. But it's OK, the ocean was underneath, broke my fall.
ALISTAIR	The Pacific Ocean?
COLIN	Yeh. The surf wasn't too high, only fifteen metres or so.
ALISTAIR	Brill.
COLIN	'Course the sharks were a problem.
ALISTAIR	Sharks!
COLIN	White pointers. There were a couple of them. Reminded me of the time I had to fight crocs off in the Territory.
ALISTAIR	Crocodiles?
COLIN	Twenty-footers. I gave them a wrestle for their money, but.
ALISTAIR	Do you know Crocodile Dundee?
COLIN	He's a mate of mine, gave me a few tips. See, a croc's got no brains. You can outsmart 'em. Not like sharks. Only way with sharks is to out-swim them.
ALISTAIR	You can out-swim sharks?
COLIN	All Australians can. Wouldn't be any of us left if we couldn't. Alistair, don't you ever get bored?
ALISTAIR	No. Well, a bit. Sometimes.

COLIN	How would you like to help me save Luke's life?
ALISTAIR	I'm not allowed to give blood!
COLIN	You don't have to give blood. Listen, do you reckon the Queen's doctor would be the best doctor in the world?
ALISTAIR	Yes, pretty good, specially cos he'd have to do it without looking.
COLIN	Eh?
ALISTAIR	Well, he would, wouldn't he? I mean if the Queen was sick he couldn't just say, 'take your frock off your Majesty and let me look at your... er... your... you know', could he? I mean, not the Queen. Nobody could, could they? He'd have to guess what's wrong. He'd have to be good.
COLIN	Er... yeh. Anyway, I wrote to her and asked her to let me get in touch with him, and she didn't write back.
ALISTAIR	When did you write to her?
COLIN	Nearly a week ago.
ALISTAIR	Well, there you are then. It'll be months before she gets round to it.
COLIN	She a bit slack?
ALISTAIR	No, not her. But hundreds of people write to her. She gets sackfuls of letters every day. Special vans full of letters for her.
COLIN	I've seen them. They've got Royal Mail written on them.
ALISTAIR	Er, yeh. Takes a bit of time to answer all them letters.
COLIN	Well, I haven't got time, I'm going to have to get into the palace and talk to her myself. And you're gonna help me.

ALISTAIR	You want me to help you break into Buckingham Palace?!
COLIN	Someone has to give me a leg up.
ALISTAIR	Mum doesn't let me go into town by myself.
COLIN	You won't be by yourself, you'll be with me.
ALISTAIR	But you can't just climb into the palace, there'll be alarms and dogs and stuff.
COLIN	No there won't, well only corgis and they'll be asleep on the Queen's bed.
ALISTAIR	How do you know?
COLIN	It was in our papers at home. A few years ago, a bloke got into Buckingham Palace at night and next morning, when the Queen woke up he was sitting on the end of her bed, looking at her. He didn't have a single dog bite on him.
ALISTAIR	I remember that.
COLIN	If he can do it, we can.
ALISTAIR	They put him in a loony bin.
COLIN	Alright then! I'll do it myself.
ALISTAIR	I'll come.
COLIN	OK, we'll set the alarm tonight for three-thirty in the morning.
ALISTAIR	I'll stay.
COLIN	Don't be a wimp.
ALISTAIR	What if you get shot?
COLIN	OK stay then!
ALISTAIR	I'll come.

COLIN	Good one. Three-thirty then. Let's go and buy a rope. (*They start to go.*)
ALISTAIR	But I'm not allowed out in the traffic.
COLIN	Alistair, anybody'd think a bus was gonna jump the kerb and weave through all the other shoppers, carefully avoiding rubbish bins and brick walls and flatten you!
ALISTAIR	Well, one could do, couldn't it?
COLIN	Alright, I'll go and buy the rope myself.
ALISTAIR	I'll come.

Act One   Scene Fifteen

It is three-thirty in the morning. The gates of the palace appear through the darkness. The boys appear, Colin *has his map.*

Colin	I know the palace is round here somewhere.
Alistair	We're lost, I knew we'd get lost.
Colin	We're not lost.
Alistair	How do you know?
Colin	Cos I know!
Alistair	It could take days to find us. We could starve. If we don't die from the pollution.
Colin	I'll put you on the bus home if you like.
Alistair	I'll come.
Colin	Right.
Alistair	What if she wakes up and sees you sitting there and gets such a fright she wets the bed? Do you know how many years in jail you'd get for making the Queen wet the bed?
Colin	I'm not gunna break into her bedroom, dumbo! I'll wait in one of the toilets and pop into the dining room and have a word when she's at breakfast.

A Policeman *strolls past.* Alistair *whimpers. The* Policeman *stops and listens.* Colin *grabs him and pulls him into the shadows. The* Policeman *ambles off, muttering something about corgis.*

Right! Let's have that rope.

ALISTAIR *opens his anorak, underneath a rope is coiled round him. They uncoil it.* COLIN *tries to lasso the top of the gates.*

ALISTAIR   Hurry up! Pretend it's one of them crocodiles.

COLIN *manages to lasso a spike on top of the gate. He tugs on the rope to test it.*

COLIN   Right, give us a leg up.

ALISTAIR *has obviously never given anyone a leg up before and there is much struggling and falling over. Finally* ALISTAIR *hoists* COLIN *up halfway.*

ALISTAIR   Oh my God, oh my God, oh my God.

COLIN   Oh no. Here we go, he's going to panic now.

ALISTAIR   Oh my God, oh my God.

COLIN   Alistair! You right down there?

ALISTAIR   Alright? Alright? We're breaking into Buckingham Palace! Sodding brilliant!

COLIN   Onya Alistair! Let's go!

ALISTAIR *heaves* COLIN *up as far as he can.* COLIN *keeps on climbing up the rope. Suddenly a brilliant spotlight flashes on them.*

ALISTAIR   Oh my God, oh my God, oh my God!

All hell breaks loose. Sirens wail, bells ring, cops come running. COLIN, *atop the gates, pinned in the light, freezes.*

COLIN   Oh, shit!

The police have brought the boys home to Iris *and* Bob's *place.*

Iris	This is the thanks we get for taking you into our home. Alistair! Stop snivelling!
Bob	We're in the computer now! The whole family in the police computer.
Iris	Out all night!
Bob	Do you know how lucky you are? You could have been charged!
Iris	You could have been killed! 'Specially you, Alistair.
Bob	I'm not having any more trouble from you two. I'll be locking those doors when we go to work!
Colin	That won't stop me! The Queen will get to my letter one day and then she'll come round here with a tank and bash the door down!
Bob	No she flippin' won't!
Colin	Yes she bloody will.
Iris	Ooh! Language. Alistair, up the stairs with you this minute. Talk to him Bob. (*She leaves with* Alistair.) Never heard such cheek in my life. Use your hanky!
Bob	You can forget the Queen, Colin my lad. She hasn't got time for the likes of you and Luke.
Colin	Bull! I've seen them on the telly visiting sick people and stuff – even lepers.
Bob	Well, what good did it ever do a leper to have his hand shook by royalty? He's still a leper. They don't leave any of their money behind on his bedside table, do they?

COLIN	She's got to help me, she's got to.
BOB	Colin, if the Queen bothered herself with solving other people's problems there would be a queue from Buckingham Palace to our back door. Don't you know why she locks herself in behind those gates?
COLIN	'Course I do, it's to keep burglars out.
BOB	To keep burglars out, and to keep her from having to bother with the likes of us!
COLIN	But people can write to her, then she doesn't have to see them and tire herself out, then she can help them.
BOB	Believe me, she won't even read your letter.
COLIN	She will.
BOB	Think about it lad, you know she won't.
COLIN	Well, what's she there for if she doesn't help people? What's all that money and all those cars and houses and armies and stuff for?
BOB	She's there, crippling us with taxes to keep her in the lap of luxury just so we can point to her and say we got a Queen.
COLIN	That's not much use to anyone.
BOB	You hit the nail on the head there, lad. Nope, if you've got something needs fixing, take a leaf out of my book and do it yourself.
COLIN	(*thoughtfully*) Do it yourself...
BOB	Stand you in good stead if you remember that. Don't see me running to the Queen every time my roof leaks or my car breaks down or I get in the police computer, do you?
COLIN	Yeh... do it yourself!

BOB	Only way, lad.
COLIN	Bugger the Queen, eh?
BOB	Yes, well. Um… Watch your language around your Auntie Iris eh?
COLIN	Yeh, alright.
BOB	Better get yourself a bit of shut-eye then.
COLIN	Yeh.

They leave.

ALISTAIR *is in his room. He is tying a lasso knot in his dressing-gown cord and practising his throw.* COLIN *enters carrying a phone book.*

ALISTAIR	Have they gone to work?
COLIN	Just.
ALISTAIR	Have they locked us in?
COLIN	Tight as a chook's bum. You even got locks on your windows in your house.
ALISTAIR	Yeh, well, can't be too careful.
COLIN	Hey, what you reckon the best cancer hospital in London would be under – H for hospital, or C for cancer?
ALISTAIR	R.
COLIN	What?
ALISTAIR	For Royal. Everything important here's called the Royal something.
COLIN	There's the Royal Children's Hospital … The Royal Automobile Club … Royal Bar and Grill … Royale Fish Shop … No Royal Cancer Hospital.
ALISTAIR	Try under Her Majesty's.
COLIN	(*looking*) Nuh. No cancer hospital.
ALISTAIR	Try under Queen Elizabeth.
COLIN	I reckon I'll just go out and find it. Got a screwdriver?
ALISTAIR	What for?

COLIN	To take the lock off the back door.
ALISTAIR	You can't do that! They'll go bananas.
COLIN	I'll be back before they are and I'll put it back on – they'll never know.
ALISTAIR	Well, you can't. All the tools are outside in the garage.
COLIN	Not to worry. (*He pulls out his Swiss army knife and leaves.*)
ALISTAIR	No! Don't! We'll get killed! That's a new lock that is! From the biggest hardware centre in Greater London. They'll kill us. I'm not supposed to be having stress. What about my dandruff? (*He rubs his head and checks out the dandruff.*) Oooohhh. It's stress that does it. I'll be out in a rash next and Mum'll kill me. I'll be having an asthma attack, sure to. (*He wheezes.*)

COLIN *re-enters with the lock and chucks it at* ALISTAIR *who catches it as though it was red-hot and throws it back.* ALISTAIR *leaps into his bed and pulls the cover over his head.*

	I don't care! Do what you like! I don't want to know! I can't see a thing – don't know anything.
COLIN	See ya, Alistair.
ALISTAIR	On your own head be it!

COLIN *carefully places the lock on the top of the mound of blankets which is* ALISTAIR*'s head and goes.*

A row of patients in wheelchairs are lined up like dummies for inspection by STUDENT DOCTORS *to the sound of loud pompous music. A puffed-up, suave and distinguished looking male* DOCTOR *enters.* COLIN *enters and a* NURSE *approaches him.*

NURSE   You lost luv?

COLIN   Is this the best cancer hospital in London?

NURSE   It's the best in the world.

COLIN   I'm not lost then.

NURSE   That's good. (*She goes back to the patients.*)

DOCTOR   (*holding up a* PATIENT's *hand to feel the pulse and speaking in a plummy voice*) Accessibility is paramount. (*The* STUDENTS *scribble in their notepads.*) The patient must always feel that he can speak to you, that you have time for him. (*to* PATIENT) And how are we today? (*There is no reply from the* PATIENT, *the* DOCTOR *drops the hand.*) That's the ticket. Next? (*He moves to the next* PATIENT *and has a listen through his stethoscope. He shouts in the* PATIENT's *ear.*) Feeling better are we? (*There is no reply.*) Good, good. (*He starts to move to the next one.*)

COLIN   'Scuse me butting in... (*The* DOCTOR *sweeps past him.*) I know you're real busy here and everything, but I'd really appreciate it if you'd come to Australia and fix Luke up. They reckon he's gunna die, but I reckon they're just slack and you could fix him.

DOCTOR   Who is this?

COLIN   Luke, my brother.

48

DOCTOR   I mean, who is this boy?

The STUDENTS *look at one another in alarm. One of them looks at his notepad.*

COLIN   We'll pay your fare. Or if you've got a jet of your own we'll pay the petrol.

DOCTOR   Remove this! At once!

The STUDENTS *try to grab* COLIN. *He runs rings round them.*

COLIN   You got to help, Luke's got cancer, he could die!

DOCTOR   Everyone here has got cancer! They could all die!!

There is a big silence, one STUDENT *clears his throat, another studies his toe-caps. The* PATIENTS' *heads swivel in unison towards the doctor.*

DOCTOR   If your brother has got … (*He lowers his voice for the word.*) cancer, there are proper channels.

COLIN   Please… just listen to me for a minute…

DOCTOR   I will not have my ward round disrupted like this!

COLIN   You've got to do it. It'll only take you a few days. You've got to!

DOCTOR   Out! Out with him at once!

The DOCTOR *leaves, the* STUDENTS *and the* NURSE *wheel out the remaining patients.*

COLIN   (*yelling*) You know what you are? You're the worst doctor in the world, you hear me? The worst doctor in the world! (*He starts to cry and then pulls himself together.*) Alright Colin mate, don't start blubbering. Dad wouldn't blubber. Not even the time you bowled a Brett Lee special off an extra long run-up and it bounced off a cow pat and slammed him in the privates. Nothin' to blubber about. You went for the

TED   What, cancer?

COLIN   Yeah, cancer.

TED   Cancer cancer cancer cancer cancer.

COLIN   Cancer cancer cancer cancer cancer.

They start to laugh.

COLIN   I'm as dry as a creek at Christmas.

TED   Pardon?

COLIN   I'm thirsty.

TED   There's a caff here in the hospital.

COLIN   My shout.

TED   Huh?

COLIN   I'm buying.

TED   You're on!

In the hospital cafeteria there are a few tables and a woman in a hospital volunteer uniform. TED *and* COLIN *approach and sit at a table.* TED *is still laughing. A few miserable looking people sit at other tables.*

TED   You actually climbed the gates of Buckingham Palace! Colin, you're an inspiration. You're better than a doctor. (*The* WOMAN *approaches.*) Six chocolate frogs please, love.

COLIN   Six chocolate frogs?!

TED   Wait and see.

COLIN   What's that say on your hand?

TED   This? It's Welsh. It means forever.

COLIN   That's nice. Nicer than a picture of a snake or love and hate tattooed on your fingers.

TED   Where I come from in Wales, people get them done when they're in love.

COLIN   Oh yeh? Has your friend got one then?

TED   Yes, my friend's got one. (*The* WOMAN *puts a box on the table.*)

WOMAN   There's ten left in the box.

TED   I'd better take the lot, then. (*He gives the* WOMAN *some money.*) Hold these, Colin. (TED *addresses the people in the cafe.*) Excuse me ladies and gentlemen. Excuse me. If you could see your faces. What a load of misery-guts. Look, we're all here for the same reason. We've all got people in there who need us very much. What they don't need is to look at a load of miserable faces.

So, if anyone here thinks they might be turning into a misery-guts, I'd strongly recommend a chocolate frog from my young friend here.

The people in the cafe look at TED *and* COLIN *like they are mad.* COLIN *looks really embarrassed. He offers the frogs round. After a moment someone takes one. The tension is broken, people smile and accept a frog.*

WOMAN	I'll have to order some more of those in.
TED	Tell you what. (*He hands* COLIN *a pen and paper.*) Write down the name of the hospital Luke's in for me.
COLIN	Why?
TED	I know a couple of doctors here pretty well. They're top people. I could have a word with them about Luke.
COLIN	Ripper. I mean yes – please.
TED	OK. Why don't you meet me here, say Wednesday at midday, we'll go see them.
COLIN	Could we make it tomorrow? I'm in a bit of a hurry.
TED	I'll do my best.

Colin is shouting down the phone to his Mum in Australia.

COLIN   Yes, yes, Auntie Iris said I could, just this once ... No, no you get used to the cold. How's Luke ... Oh ... Well it won't be for much longer ... No, you don't understand. See, I got great news ... No ... Yes ... Mum, listen to me a minute ... Listen! I'm going to see one of London's top cancer doctors. Tomorrow. Luke's going to be cured ... Are you there? Mum? Your voice sounds funny ... Did you hear what I said? I'm fixing it up tomorrow. It's all going to be alright now ... Don't cry ... Let go of what? I can't understand a word you're saying. (**BOB** *enters.*) I better go. Uncle Bob's pointing at his watch. Bye Mum, see you all soon. Bye.

BOB   Alright then?

COLIN   She always cries when she's happy.

Bob puts his arm round Colin's shoulders.

In ALISTAIR's *bedroom.* COLIN *is punching numbers on a mobile phone.*

ALISTAIR	You won't get away with it again, you know.
COLIN	Hello, Qantas? Could you tell me please which days this week you've got empty seats for Australia?
ALISTAIR	You fluked it yesterday, but if you take that lock off again, they'll find out.
COLIN	No, it's not a school project…
ALISTAIR	I'm warning you…
COLIN	Shush a minute. Now, they can't be near the dunnies, one of the passengers is a very eminent doctor. I see, you never put eminent doctors near the dunnies. That's good.
ALISTAIR	We'll be eating cold baked beans for a week.
COLIN	Shurrup! No, sorry, not you. Yes, thank you very much. I'll let you know. Bye. (COLIN *takes out his Swiss army knife and holds it up and winks at* ALISTAIR.) See ya Alistair.

ALISTAIR *makes a lunge for the knife. They tumble and wrestle.* ALISTAIR *comes out better and gets his arm round* COLIN's *neck.*

	Gaaarrrggg! Lemme go! You're chokin' me.
ALISTAIR	Give me that knife then.
COLIN	Alright, alright, but you're gonna be responsible.
ALISTAIR	What are you on about?
COLIN	If I don't get the doctor to Luke, it'll be your fault.

ALISTAIR	Oh yeh? First it was the Queen, now it's the best doctor in the world dropping everything to go to Australia with you. Pull the other one.
COLIN	It's true. I'm meeting him today. Straight up.
ALISTAIR	The world's best doctor's meeting you?
COLIN	Today at noon. I met this bloke, see, who knows him. He's arranging it. Luke's gonna be cured. It's all set.
ALISTAIR	Honest?
COLIN	I told you, straight up.
ALISTAIR	Sodding brilliant. Just wait till you get back to Australia. You're going to be a blinking hero you are. (**He hands** COLIN **the knife.**)
COLIN	Some hero with a broken neck.
ALISTAIR	Sorry. Hey, you will be back before, you know, before they, you know.
COLIN	No worries.
ALISTAIR	It's just that I hate cold baked beans.
COLIN	Yeh? Well I love'em.

He leaves.

TED is waiting. He looks a proper misery-guts. COLIN enters and hands him a chocolate frog. TED looks up and smiles.

TED	Hi digger.
COLIN	Is it all set?
TED	The doctor's meeting us here in a minute.
COLIN	He a quick packer?
TED	What?
COLIN	A quick packer. Or is he like Annie Strachan's Mum, always making lists and losing them.

A woman in a white coat walks towards them.

TED	Colin...
COLIN	Doesn't matter. He won't need much. And Dad can always lend him a couple of shirts – unless he's got a really fat neck.
TED	Colin, this is Doctor Graham.

The DOCTOR holds out her hand.

DOCTOR	Hello, Colin.
COLIN	(*shaking it*) G'day.
TED	Dr Graham is one of the most experienced cancer experts in the world.
COLIN	Great. When can you leave? They've got seats on all flights, including tonight.
DOCTOR	Colin, it's not that simple.
COLIN	You don't have to worry about getting a seat near the dunnies...

DOCTOR	I've been in touch with the hospital in Sydney where Luke is.
COLIN	Excellent. Dad always says 'If you want a job done, go to the top ma—... er... woman.'
DOCTOR	I rang early this morning and I talked to one of the doctors treating Luke. He's in good hands, Colin. They're the best in Luke's unit.
COLIN	Mum and Dad will want to pay you back for that call.
DOCTOR	The doctor explained to me exactly what type of cancer Luke has. His prognosis is correct. Luke can't be cured.
TED	Colin, I'm...
COLIN	BULL!
DOCTOR	He's going to die, Colin.
COLIN	BULL!
DOCTOR	The exact location and the advanced stage of the disease means Luke is one of the unlucky ones...
COLIN	BULL!
DOCTOR	It's very rare...
COLIN	(*running off, yelling*) Bull!

TED *calls after him and then runs after him, the* DOCTOR *leaves.*

Act Two Scene Twenty-four

Colin enters Alistair's bedroom, completely wrung out and lies down on his bed. Iris and Bob and Alistair hover outside the room.

Bob He's just sort of lying there.

Iris It's delayed shock. Alistair, leave your scalp alone.

Bob Had to happen sooner or later, poor kid. You heard your mother.

Iris I wonder if we should get the doctor in?

Bob No, plenty of rest and he'll be right as rain.

Iris Let's leave him in peace then.

They tiptoe out. Alistair tiptoes back and sits beside Colin.

Alistair Didn't it work out then?

Colin They tricked me.

Alistair Who tricked you?

Colin They reckon he can't be cured. He said he knew the best doctor in the world. I phoned Mum and everything.

Alistair I reckon you won't be going home a hero then.

Colin I can't go home now. Ever.

Alistair Great. I'll be a nervous wreck by the time we grow up.

Colin I can't face them. I promised I'd make it alright.

Alistair We're only kids. We're not supposed to make everything alright.

Pause.

	I was reading this book about ancient tribes in the Amazon. Do you know, they never get things like heart disease and other, you know, things.
COLIN	Cancer?
ALISTAIR	It's an unknown disease up the Amazon, is that.

COLIN *sits up.*

COLIN	Maybe they do get it, but they know how to cure it.
ALISTAIR	I shouldn't think so, not ancient tribes.
COLIN	Maybe while we've been using up all our technology on spaceships and computers and stuff they've been quietly discovering a cure for cancer. I've got to go there!
ALISTAIR	Do you know how much that would cost?!
COLIN	I've got my return ticket to Australia, I can have a stop-over.
ALISTAIR	Your plane won't be going past the Amazon.
COLIN	Well, I'll stow away on a cargo ship.
ALISTAIR	You're soft, you are.
COLIN	I'll go down the docks tomorrow and jump a cargo ship to South America.
ALISTAIR	But what about snake bites and cholera and cannibals and stuff?
COLIN	It'll be worth it to see Mum's face when I walk into that hospital with the cure.
ALISTAIR	You want locking up, you do.
COLIN	Tried that, remember?
ALISTAIR	Just don't tell me any more about it. Mum says she's never seen my dandruff so bad. I can't take the stress.

COLIN	I wonder what time high tide is?

Pause.

ALISTAIR	Colin… ?
COLIN	Here we go. Alright, what problem have you thought of this time?
ALISTAIR	Well, like, you'll need someone to give you a leg up and help you hack through the jungle and stuff. I'd better come.
COLIN	OK.
ALISTAIR	When did you say we're leaving?
COLIN	Tomorrow, the quicker the better.
ALISTAIR	Good.

Pause.

	I didn't think you were going to make it back in time today.
COLIN	Yeh, well I had things to do.
ALISTAIR	What, like?
COLIN	Reckon they're so smart. I fixed them.
ALISTAIR	What have you done this time?

COLIN *takes out his knife and demonstrates slashing tyres.*

COLIN	Some of those fancy doctors are going to be late for their fancy dinners at their fancy houses cos they got no air in the tyres of their fancy cars any more.
ALISTAIR	Oh God.
COLIN	I slashed them to pieces. I would have done them all if Ted hadn't found me.

ALISTAIR   You know what you've done, don't you? You've gone and dropped him right in it.

COLIN   What are you rabbiting on about? I did it, he's alright.

ALISTAIR   It was him that took you there.

COLIN   (*realising*) I'd better go see if he's alright tomorrow.

ALISTAIR   I thought we were going to South America tomorrow?

COLIN   Next day, alright?

ALISTAIR   Alright.

Act Two   Scene Twenty-five

At Ted's place. TED *is moving around with great difficulty. The doorbell rings.*

TED   Who is it?

COLIN   (*from outside*) It's me, Colin Mudford.

TED   The key's under next door's mat.

COLIN   Next door's?

TED   You don't think I'm daft enough to leave it under mine in a neighbourhood like this do you? Go and fetch it and let yourself in.

TED *struggles to a chair. By the time he has done so,* COLIN *has entered.*

COLIN   Oh no, Alistair was right. They bashed you up.

TED   You what?

COLIN   The doctors, they bashed you up cos of their tyres.

TED   The doctors didn't bash me up.

COLIN   They'll be looking for me then.

TED   No, actually they're looking for an Irish tow-truck driver with a red beard and a limp. I told them that's who I saw letting the air out of their tyres.

COLIN   Lucky for them I only let the air out instead of slashing them to bits.

TED   Lucky for you, you mean.

COLIN   Did you have an accident?

TED   Not exactly. Local hoons jumped me last night as I was leaving the hospital. Belted me round the head with a

64

lump of wood and jumped up and down on me a bit. Hurt my foot.

COLIN	Why?
TED	I don't think they like me.
COLIN	Did you tell the police?
TED	They don't like me much either. Anyway, I didn't get a good look at them. (*He winces as he tries to move.*)
COLIN	I reckon you better go to bed.
TED	No can do. I've got to get to a phone somehow and let the hospital know I can't visit. Griff'll be frantic when I don't turn up.
COLIN	I'll visit her for you – if you like.

TED *looks at* COLIN. *He gets his wallet out and takes a photo from it and hands it to him.*

TED	That's Griff.
COLIN	Oh.

Pause.

I'll visit him for you if you like.

TED	(*smiling*) Well, maybe if you just phone for me.
COLIN	Is that why they bashed you up, cos you and Griff are in love? (TED *nods.*) I don't mind going to the hospital for you, honest.
TED	That's very good of you, but…
COLIN	No worries.
TED	Colin… Griff hasn't just got cancer. He's got AIDS.
COLIN	But there's drugs you can get, I've read about it.

TED   Griff is one of the unlucky ones. I don't expect you
               want to go to the hospital any more.

COLIN   What time's visiting hours?

          Pause.

TED   Give us your shoulder. I got a few things in the kitchen
               you can take to him for me.

In the hospital garden. GRIFF is wheeled in in a wheelchair. He is wearing a bright scarf over his head tied behind his neck. He is very frail.

NURSE   Well, think you've had enough fresh air?

GRIFF   Can I just sit out here a while?

NURSE   It's a bit chilly, love.

GRIFF   A few minutes, please.

NURSE   Just a few minutes.

The NURSE tucks a blanket round GRIFF's shoulders and leaves as COLIN enters.

COLIN   Are you Griff Price?

GRIFF   Yes.

COLIN   I'm Colin, a friend of Ted's. He's a bit crook today. It's OK but, it's nothing serious. He wrote you this note.

GRIFF reads the note.

GRIFF   (*trying to be composed*) Did his doctor say how many days before he can walk?

COLIN   Don't think so. You don't look much like your picture.

GRIFF   I know. When I look in the mirror I give myself a fright.

COLIN   No, you look... um... (*He indicates the scarf.*) ... Nice.

GRIFF   The treatment made my hair fall out.

COLIN   (*embarrassed*) It... er... suits you.

GRIFF   Thank you, kind sir.

COLIN   Ted sent you this. (*He gives* GRIFF *a brown paper bag,* GRIFF *opens it.*)

GRIFF   Tangerines! Oh, Colin, you're an angel!

COLIN   You like them?

GRIFF   Been craving for them, can't eat much any more. I always thought that when I saw my first angel it would have wings and a halo, not freckles and elastic-sided boots!

As GRIFF *peels a tangerine, a* NURSE *strolls by with someone in a wheelchair. The* NURSE *helps the patient up and they walk into the hospital leaving the wheelchair behind.*

           Want some? (*He holds out half a tangerine.*) Or would you rather peel your own?

COLIN   Thanks. (*He takes the half tangerine.*) How long have you and Ted known each other?

GRIFF   Six years. I met him in a sheet-metal factory in Wales. We both had jobs there.

COLIN   Why did you leave?

GRIFF   Factory closed down last year. Spent months looking for work. So we decided to try our luck in the big smoke.

COLIN   How did you go?

GRIFF   A week after we got here I got sick. They did a few tests and told me I'd got AIDS. I haven't been too well since, so Ted took care of me till I had to come in here. (*GRIFF rubs his finger gently over the tattoo on his hand.*)

COLIN   I know what that means. It's Welsh for forever.

GRIFF	Forever.
COLIN	You'll be out of here soon. Prob'ly.
GRIFF	One way or another.

Pause.

	It's very good of you to visit me. I appreciate it.
COLIN	It's alright.
GRIFF	Don't get many visitors.
COLIN	It's too far for your Mum and Dad to come every day?
GRIFF	They don't come.
COLIN	Not ever?
TED	I'm not their favourite person.
COLIN	Why?
GRIFF	Me and Ted, and… this. They can't accept things. (*He changes the subject.*) Do you miss the Aussie sunshine?
COLIN	A bit.
GRIFF	When things got tough in Wales, we used to dream about emigrating to Australia; everybody here does. What do you do over there for a cheer-up?
COLIN	Um… We got Arnie Strachan.
GRIFF	Tell me about Arnie Strachan.
COLIN	He's got pet chooks.
GRIFF	Chooks?
COLIN	Chickens. He loves them chooks. Gave them all names. Hey, one day Doug Beal drove his trail bike into Arnie's Chook pen. Arnie was as mad as a cut

snake – he got his Dad's sheep clippers and went round Doug's place and sheared his Mum's shagpile carpet!

GRIFF   Ow, don't make me laugh like that! It hurts!

COLIN   Sorry.

GRIFF   No, I like it. We don't get much to laugh at in here. What are you doing over here anyway?

COLIN   I'm... I'm on holiday.

The NURSE *returns for* GRIFF.

NURSE   Sorry, rest time, no more nattering.

GRIFF   Alright bossy. Will you come and see me again Colin? I'd like to get to know Arnie Strachan.

COLIN   Yeh, alright.

GRIFF   And tell Ted to hurry up and get better, eh?

COLIN   Don't worry. You'll be seeing him soon.

The NURSE *leaves with* GRIFF. COLIN *spies the empty wheelchair and puts his hand on it.*

Sooner than you think!

COLIN *looks furtively around him then makes a run for it with the empty wheelchair.*

In the hospital garden. Suddenly there are shrieks and laughter from out of sight. COLIN *races in pushing* GRIFF *in his wheelchair.* TED *frantically pushes the wheels of the stolen wheelchair in an effort to catch up. They do wheelies and come to a halt, laughing.*

GRIFF	I'm still faster than you are.
TED	I'm handicapped and you've got that Aussie racing goanna on your side.

The NURSE *enters and looks at them frowning.* TED *pulls a rug up under his chin and looks innocent.* COLIN *and* GRIFF *also look angelic. The* NURSE *finds a spot some distance away and gets out her lunch.*

GRIFF	You've worn me out.
TED	(*concerned*) Are you alright?
GRIFF	Never better. But no more what d'you call them? Wheelies?
TED	You know what you are, Colin? A genius.
COLIN	Could you put that in writing? I'll send it to Mr Blair at school.
GRIFF	(*tenderly, to* TED) It's good to see you. I was worried.
COLIN	I reckon I'll just... um...

COLIN *leaves them and approaches the* NURSE. TED *and* GRIFF *in the background talk earnestly and quietly.*

	G'day.
NURSE	Hello. You're getting to be a regular.

COLIN	I reckon.
NURSE	(*looking in* TED's *direction*) Funny, I can't place that patient with Mr Price. Sure I've seen him before though.
COLIN	Ah, he's, ah, from another ward.
NURSE	Oh. Mr Price looks happy. I think you cheer him up. You know he's… quite sick.
COLIN	Yes.
NURSE	They all are in here.
COLIN	It's weird. Some of the people in here…
NURSE	What?
COLIN	I just noticed. Some of them don't look like they're going to die. I mean they look real crook and everything, but they don't look… miserable.
NURSE	Some cope better than others. I think it's the families that make all the difference. If they all rally round, I don't know, it seems to help.
COLIN	I reckon you're right.
NURSE	Oops, look at the time! I got to get back. Bye.
COLIN	See ya.

TED *beckons* COLIN *over.*

TED	Colin, I know you probably don't like soppy stuff. But we wanted to say thanks.
GRIFF	You'll probably never know how important this little bit of time is to us, or how precious a gift you've given us.
TED	Now that was soppy!

They leave.

Act Two   Scene Twenty-eight

At Alistair's house. He is practising hacking through the jungle with the bread-knife. He has a colander on his head. Iris *walks past.*

Iris	Nice game, love?
Alistair	Er... yes Mum.
Iris	Well, don't go wearing yourself out, pet.

She leaves. Colin *walks past.*

Colin	What are you doing?
Alistair	(*whispering*) I'm practising for the jungle. I made us a grappling iron out of coathangers to get on the cargo ship.
Colin	Great.
Alistair	Tomorrow, right?
Colin	Well...
Alistair	You said tomorrow a week ago! And three days ago! And yesterday!
Colin	I've got to meet Ted tomorrow and help put that wheelchair back.
Alistair	You're going to get caught, they're coming home early tomorrow.
Colin	I'll be back in time. You should see how happy Griff is...
Alistair	That's all very well, but the ancient tribes of the Amazon are probably giving their cure for cancer to some drug company who'll put it into pills and sell them for a million pounds. Each.

COLIN	It won't be much longer. Promise. Hey – where's Wales?
ALISTAIR	Wales? WALES?!!
COLIN	Can you get the tube there?
ALISTAIR	It's another bloomin' country is Wales!
COLIN	Oh. Pity. There's some people there need a good talking to.

COLIN *leaves.*

ALISTAIR	The two explorers hack through the jungle. Hack! Hack! The tsetse flies and the leeches and the heat drive them mad. Hack! Hack! And all the time the sound of the cannibals' drums gets louder and louder … Hack! Hack! Suddenly a cobra springs out of the undergrowth and sinks its fangs into the wimpy explorer's hand. Help! Help! he cries as he sinks to his knees in the quicksand. I'll save you! says the tough explorer. He cuts into the flesh with his trusty blade and puts the wimpy explorer's hand to his lips and starts to suck out the poison...

ALISTAIR *sucks his arm and spits and sucks noisily again.* IRIS *enters.*

IRIS	Alistair! What are you doing?
ALISTAIR	Er… Nothing…
IRIS	Get upstairs at once. I don't know what gets into you.

ALISTAIR *goes.* IRIS *watches him, worried.*

Kissing his hand now! Maybe I should get him one of those child psychiatrists. Bob! (*She goes.*)

At the hospital. TED *wheels* GRIFF *on.* GRIFF's *head hangs, his eyes are closed. His hand falls over the side of the wheelchair arm rest.* TED *stops and tenderly replaces it. A* NURSE *enters and feels for* GRIFF's *pulse.* COLIN *enters bearing a bag of tangerines. He realises* GRIFF *has died and places the bag on* GRIFF's *lap. The* NURSE *wheels* GRIFF *off.*

COLIN	I'm glad he wasn't alone.
TED	It wasn't enough. He asked for them.
COLIN	His family?

TED *nods.*

COLIN	Couldn't you get them to come?
TED	No.
COLIN	Pikers.
TED	They'll come now, they'll take him back to Wales for the funeral.
COLIN	They've got no right!
TED	It's alright, it's where he needs to be. Home, see? Colin, will you do me a favour?
COLIN	Sure.
TED	Stay with me a while?
COLIN	Sure.

Act Two Scene Thirty

At Alistair's house. There are yowls from out of sight. Iris *leads* Alistair *in by the ear. She has the back door lock in her hand.*

Iris	I'll give you sorry, my lad.
Alistair	Ow ow ow ow ow ow!
Iris	What else have you two been up to?
Alistair	It wasn't me it was him!
Iris	What have I told you about lies?
Alistair	He said he'd torture me if I told.
Iris	Nothing but trouble since he got here.
Alistair	I tried to stop him, Mum – honest.
Colin	Alistair! I'm back. (*He enters.*) Oh-oh.
Iris	I'm very, very disappointed in you Colin Mudford. We invited you over here to take your mind off… things and all you've done is lie to us and deceive us.
Colin	Sorry.
Iris	South America! Are you out of your mind? Do you know what the sun does to Alistair's rash?
Colin	Sorry.
Iris	Bit late for that now, after you've been gallivanting all over London with unsuitable types.
Colin	I haven't…
Iris	Don't try and deny it.
Colin	They weren't unsuitable.

IRIS	How do we know that, when we haven't even had the pleasure of meeting them?
COLIN	Well, actually…
IRIS	I don't want to hear any more from you young man. Upstairs with you and it's cold baked beans for tea – for you both! And be grateful!

She goes.

ALISTAIR	Sorry I blabbed, but I was being tortured… (COLIN *looks at him contemptuously.*) Well, actually, Mum told me keeping secrets would make my dandruff worse.
COLIN	Doesn't matter. If the ancient tribes had a cure for cancer, we'd have seen it on TV by now.
ALISTAIR	Prob'ly. You won't be able to see Ted any more.
COLIN	Oh yes I will.
ALISTAIR	(ALISTAIR *covers his ears.*) Don't tell me, I don't want to know.
COLIN	I've invited him here to tea.
ALISTAIR	(*starts whistling*) I can't hear you. (*whistles*) I'm not listening.
COLIN	Tomorrow.

Iris wheels a tea trolley in, Bob places some chairs around.
Alistair joins them and they sit formally. Alistair reaches for a
biscuit from the trolley, Iris slaps his hand. A kitsch doorbell
is heard and they jump up in apprehension. Colin tears out of
the room in his usual bullet-fashion.

Colin   I'll get it! (*He returns with Ted.*) Auntie Iris, Uncle Bob,
this is my mate, Ted. The one with his mouth hangin'
open is my cousin Alistair.

Alistair shuts his mouth, there are 'pleased-to-meet-yous' all
round. Ted is sat down. They all look at each other smiling
stiffly and then all say something at once.

Iris   Cup of tea, Ted?

Ted   Thank you. (*Iris starts to pour, Alistair grabs the*
opportunity to take a biscuit.) Nice home you have.

Iris   Thank you Ted. Bob's a bit of a do-it-yourself
enthusiast.

Bob   Only way. I'm not paying hundreds of pounds to some
cowboy to mess up my plumbing, eh?

Ted   Quite right.

Bob   You into home improvements?

Ted   Er, no, not much.

Iris   The biggest hardware centre in Greater London's not
far from here. Bob could show you round.

Ted   Another time perhaps.

Bob   What do you do for a crust, Ted?

TED	I'm unemployed.
COLIN	He's not a dole-bludger, but. He had to stay home and look after Griff.

TED looks like he is going to cry. His teacup starts to wobble. He puts it on the trolley.

IRIS	Top up, Ted? (*He shakes his head.*) Biscuit? Piece of cake?

Suddenly IRIS picks up a bowl from the trolley. She hands it round (missing ALISTAIR) everybody takes a tangerine.

They're lovely, these. Take your mind off… things.

TED begins to cry. IRIS motions to BOB to take ALISTAIR out of the room. He does so. There is silence as TED cries. COLIN is struggling not to cry too. TED pulls himself together a little.

(*kindly*) Would you like your cup of tea now, love?

TED tries to answer, but he cannot. COLIN, his voice very shaky, answers for him.

COLIN	He'll be right, thanks.
TED	(*to* COLIN) I think I'd better go. (*to* IRIS) Thanks very much.
IRIS	You don't have to go, love. Stay until you feel better.
TED	No, I'll be alright now.
IRIS	Are you sure?
TED	Thank you, yes.
IRIS	Alright, take care of yourself then.
TED	Thanks.
IRIS	Bye then.

COLIN *sees* TED *off.* IRIS *studies the tangerines, puzzled.* COLIN *re-enters. He stands looking at his Auntie* IRIS. *He starts to cry.*

COLIN	I want to go home.
IRIS	Oh pet.

IRIS *holds out her arms.* COLIN *runs to her and cries in her arms loud and long. As he quietens,* BOB *and* ALISTAIR *return.*

BOB	Alright, then?
IRIS	He's alright, aren't you love?
COLIN	Yeh.
IRIS	Bit homesick, that's all.
COLIN	It's not just that. I've got to go home.
IRIS	You will, love, when things are... you know.
COLIN	You don't understand. I have to go home and be with Luke.
IRIS	You can't love.
BOB	You don't really want to go back to all that, do you?
COLIN	Yes.
IRIS	No you don't.
ALISTAIR	Yes he does.
IRIS	Shut up Alistair.
COLIN	I got to go, auntie.
ALISTAIR	See.
BOB	You heard your mother, Alistair.
COLIN	Please.
ALISTAIR	Go on, let him.

BOB *points out of the room and* ALISTAIR *shuffles off.* BOB *gives him a hurry-up and follows.*

COLIN   You can't stop me. I have to go home!

IRIS   Now listen to me, love, put it out of your mind, you can't go home. You'll understand when you're older that it's for the best.

COLIN   No! You're wrong!

IRIS   Now stop this nonsense.

COLIN   I told you, I'm going home!

IRIS   Listen to me Colin. I'm sorry things are so hard for you love, but you're not going to Australia, and that's that. And just in case you and Alistair have got any notions of cooking something up, don't waste your time. They won't let you on the plane without a guardian to sign the forms. Now, I don't want to hear another word about it. OK? OK??

COLIN   OK. I won't mention it again.

IRIS   There's a good lad.

Act Two   Scene Thirty-two

At the airport. There is a small counter with a woman behind it. Ted paces up and down. Colin enters lugging his suitcase.

TED   I thought you weren't going to make it.

COLIN   Yeh, took me a while to figure out how to get the new lock off.

TED   Nobody woke up, then?

COLIN   Snoring their heads off.

TED   Better get checked in.

They go to the desk. The Woman takes Colin's case and his ticket.

WOMAN   Travelling alone?

COLIN   Yes.

WOMAN   (*to Ted*) What relationship are you to the traveller?

COLIN   Mate.

TED   Friend.

WOMAN   Guardian?

COLIN   That's right.

WOMAN   Sign here please, so the young man can travel unaccompanied. (*Ted signs.*)

TED   (*They walk away from the desk.*) Well, this is it then.

COLIN   I hope you don't get into trouble, signing and stuff.

TED   Nah. Besides, I'm used to trouble. Think about me sometimes… and Griff.

COLIN   I got you a present. Here. (COLIN *digs in his pocket and hands* TED *a pink scarf.*)

TED   Great! My favourite colour.

They hug. TED *puts the scarf on and flips it over his shoulder.*

               See ya Colin.

COLIN   See ya Ted.

TED *leaves.*

Act Two   Scene Thirty-three

Auntie Iris *and Uncle* Bob *rush in.* Alistair *puffs up behind.*

Iris	STOP! Stop that boy!
Colin	Shit!

Colin *makes a run for it. They all try to grab him, including the airport* Woman, *there is much tripping up and tangling (some of it done by* Alistair *who is on* Colin's *side). Finally, they collar him.*

Woman	Alright, now what is going on here?
Iris	This young man is trying to leave the country illegally.
Colin	No I'm not. I'm an Australian citizen, I got my passport and I'm going home!
Iris	You're an under-age Australian citizen and you're not going anywhere!
Woman	Who exactly are you people?
Bob	I'm this boy's uncle, he's under my care.
Woman	You're his guardian?
Bob	Legal guardian I am.
Woman	But what about the man who signed the form?
Iris	Who signed? Colin, who was it? Was it your friend Ted? He's in big trouble my lad, big trouble.
Woman	I'd better get the airport police.
Colin	No! The police don't like him, please don't.
Bob	That won't be necessary, thank you very much. There's no real harm done. We'll sort things out.

Iris	Now then Colin, we're going to have no more…
Colin	The plane'll be leaving in a minute. Let me go, please?
Alistair	I think you should let him.
Iris	Shut up Alistair.
Alistair	No, really…
Bob	You heard your mother.
Colin	I've got to go.
Iris	I'm warning you Colin Mudford…
Colin	I'm going. You can't watch me every minute of the day and night! If you lock me up I'll escape…
Alistair	He will, you know.
Bob and Iris	SHUT UP Alistair!
Colin	I'll get home somehow.
Bob	Come on Colin lad, don't you think we've had enough of all this?
Alistair	(*yelling*) Enough! I'll tell you who's had enough! I've had enough, that's who's had enough! (*stunned silence*) I've got him thinking up all sorts of tricks to get me in trouble and you telling me what to do night and day. Do this Alistair, do that! Well I've had it! What makes you grown-ups so smart that you know what's best for everybody? You're not smart at all, any of you! He's the one that knows what's best for him and Luke, not you! He knows where he wants to be and he's goin' and that's final!

Silence.

Iris	Alistair… ?
Alistair	(*losing his bottle*) Sorry…

IRIS	Bob, our Alistair's growing up. Oh, Alistair.
BOB	Yes, well…
IRIS	Maybe the boy's got a point.
COLIN	Please…
IRIS	What do you think Bob?

There is a last boarding call announcement. **BOB** *ponders.*

BOB	Let the lad go home.
IRIS	I don't know what I'm going to say to your mother.
COLIN	Mum'll be right.
IRIS	Well… Be off with you then.
COLIN	I love you Auntie Iris.
IRIS	Oh, stop that.
COLIN	Onya Alistair. Oh, here, I meant to give you this. (*He gives* ALISTAIR *his Swiss army knife.*) You might need it one day.
ALISTAIR	Aw, brill!
IRIS	Alistair, give that back. You'll cut yourself.
ALISTAIR	No I won't.
IRIS	Oh. Well be careful with it then. Look after yourself Colin, love.
ALISTAIR	(*getting a letter out*) I nearly forgot. The postman brought this for you. It's from Buckingham Palace.

COLIN *opens the letter and reads aloud.*

COLIN	Dear Mr Mudford. Her Majesty's sympathies are with all who suffer through illness. May I, on her behalf, wish your brother a speedy recovery. Signed… I can't read the signature… Palace Li…

ALISTAIR   (*He had read it.*) Palace Liaison Officer – oops!

BOB   Her Majesty's sympathies! Huh!

COLIN   (*screwing the letter up and throwing it at* ALISTAIR *and mimicking* BOB) Get me started on the Queen!

ALISTAIR   (*drop-kicking it back*) Ought to be stuffed and put in a museum!

BOB   Too right! Say hello to everyone for us Colin.

COLIN   Yeh, see ya.

They kiss him.

ALISTAIR   See ya Colin.

They wave. COLIN *waves back.*

ALISTAIR   (*to* BOB) They're charging by the minute in that car park... Eh Dad?

BOB   Right son.

They hurry off toward the car park. The last call for Colin's plane is heard.

LOUDSPEAKER   Now boarding from gate number ten is Qantas flight
VOICE   number two to Sydney via Singapore and Melbourne. This is your last call, your last call for Qantas flight number two to Sydney via Singapore and Melbourne.

The BUSINESSMAN *from the flight over hurries on, he is busy checking his ticket and does not notice* COLIN.

COLIN   G'day! Fancy meeting you again!

The BUSINESSMAN *looks at* COLIN *in horror.*

What number's your ticket? Let's have a look. Hey, you've got the seat next to me again. Where you goin'?

The BUSINESSMAN *backs away, shaking his head. He turns and runs off, waving his ticket.*

You'll miss the plane! Poor bugger must have
indigestion again.

COLIN *heads for the plane.*

Luke *is in his hospital bed.* Mum *and* Dad *sit beside him.* Colin *enters.* Luke *sits up and flings his arms wide.*

Luke   Colin! Colin! Colin!

Mum *and* Dad *look up. Their faces light up.* Colin *rushes into* Luke*'s arms.*

Activities

Before you study the play
Independent research

This play is an adaptation of Morris Gleitzman's popular novel of the same name. Before you study the play, it would be helpful to know some background information about Morris Gleitzman so that you understand how this may have affected his perspective and viewpoint when writing the novel.

1   In pairs, devise a series of 15 questions about Morris Gleitzman. List them in a table like the one below.

2   Identify any links between your questions and order them so that they follow on logically from each other. Try to divide your questions into two or three main sections, for instance 'Morris Gleitzman's life' and 'Morris Gleitzman's novels'.

3   Use the internet or your library to help you find the information you need to answer your questions. Remember to list your sources of information, as in the example below.

Question	Answer	Source
1 Where does Morris Gleitzman live?	Melbourne	Morris Gleitzman's official website
2 What other novels has he written?		

While you are studying the play
Drama techniques: group sculptures

Group sculptures are a way of exploring the emotions and feelings of a range of characters at an important moment. Each person takes the role of a character from the scene and considers how that character feels at that moment. In creating the sculpture, you need to consider the spatial relationships between characters, as well as posture, stance, gesture and eye contact.

1   In scene 1, Luke faints and is taken into hospital. In a group of four, take the roles of Luke, Colin, Mum and Dad. Create a group sculpture of the moment that Luke faints.

2   Ask someone to take a digital photograph of your group sculpture. Add thought bubbles to the photograph that explain what each character is thinking.

Active reading strategies: speculation and hypothesis

As we start reading a text and begin to develop a relationship with a character, it is important that we build up a sense of the character beyond what we read on the page.

1   In scene 6, Colin is told that he is being sent to England. Imagine that you are Colin. Make a list of 20 objects that you are going to take with you to England, in addition to your clothes and shoes. Consider Colin's character and what you think he would want to take with him.

2   Add an explanation of why you think Colin would take each item with him.

3   Share your list with a partner, explaining and justifying your choices to each other. Explore whether you made the same choices or different ones and discuss your reasons for this.

Active reading strategies: inferring meaning

In order to gain a full understanding of characters, it is helpful to infer meaning about their thoughts, personalities and viewpoints. Good readers do this by exploring the clues a writer gives us about a character, rather than just what we are told directly. Look at scene 7, in which Colin is taken to the airport for his journey to England. What we can infer about Colin's character from the things that he says and does in this scene?

1   Pick out five details in scene 7 that tell you something about Colin's character. List them in a table like the one below. In the right-hand column, explain what we learn about Colin from each detail. An example has been completed for you.

Detail	What this tells us about Colin
Colin says 'Let's go.'	Either he is eager to go to England or he dislikes emotional scenes and doesn't want his mum to get emotional in the airport.

Active reading strategies: speculation and hypothesis

1 In pairs, discuss what you have learned about Colin in scenes 1 to 7. You should speculate on four focus areas: family, personality, daily activities and interests.

a) What can you **deduce** from the text? For example, we know he and his family live in Australia.

b) What can you **infer** from the text? For example, that Colin likes to tidy his bedroom.

2 As you talk, make notes on a copy of the mind map below.

Family ——————⟍   ⟋—— Daily activities
              Colin Mudford
Personality ——————⟋   ⟍—— Interests

Writing to imagine, explore and entertain

In scene 9, Colin has arrived in England to stay with his Aunt Iris, Uncle Bob and cousin Alistair. You are going to use writing to help you explore Colin's character in more detail.

1 Imagine that you are Colin. Write a letter commenting on your journey to England and giving your first impressions of your relatives. You should also explain what your plans are for your time in London. You need to show evidence that you can infer meaning from the text and explore the emotions of the character.

2 Because you are writing to explore and entertain, you should also think about the way that Colin speaks and try to write using his style and tone. Try to imitate the informative and unemotional style that Colin often uses when he speaks.

Drama techniques: improvisation

One way to get inside a character's mind is to act out their thoughts about a situation that is unfolding in front of them. In scene 10, Colin's Aunt Iris and Uncle Bob don't feel comfortable talking to him about what is happening back in Australia.

1 Working with a partner, make a list of all the questions Colin might have about the way Luke's illness has been handled, for instance, in sending him away and in not talking about it. Your aim in doing this is to understand all of Colin's concerns and worries about Luke.

2 Taking the roles of Colin and Alistair, work together to devise an improvisation of a conversation in which Colin expresses all his thoughts and concerns about how his family is reacting to Luke's death. You should try to speak and perform as if you are Colin and Alistair, using the kind of language they would use.

Drama techniques: montage

A montage is a series of images that reflects the themes, ideas, objects or emotions connected with a situation or event. Creating a montage of images and words that represents what a situation means to a character can help you to develop your understanding of the character and what might be going through their mind when faced with a situation.

1 Working with a partner and using a large sheet of paper, create a montage of images and words that summarise the thoughts that Colin might have about what London represents to him. For instance, it might include an image of Big Ben, a family (representing Iris, Bob and Alistair), the word 'new', a London bus and the word 'strange'.

2 When you have created your montage, share it with another pair, explaining the images and words you have chosen and what they mean.

3 You may also want to choose a song to use as a soundtrack. This will help your montage come to life and be heard as well as seen.

Writing to inform, explain and describe

In scene 10, Colin says that he wants to see Buckingham Palace. Alistair and Aunt Iris also recommend going to London Zoo and seeing Big Ben.

1 Write an informative web page for a teenager, telling them about local attractions and describing the things they might want to do or see. You can write about your home area or about London.

2 When writing to inform, explain and describe, remember that it is important to structure your writing and develop your ideas. You will need to consider how to present the information, for example by using sub-headings, and how you can use topic sentences that are then extended into full, detailed paragraphs. Consider whether to use the second person ('you') and the present tense. You also need to think about how formal the language you use should be, as the web page is aimed at teenagers.

Writing to argue, persuade and advise

Uncle Bob has very strong views on the monarchy and about the Queen in particular. Morris Gleitzman, the author of the novel this play is based on, is Australian. Many Australians hold strong views about the monarchy, as that makes them part of the British Commonwealth. You are going to write a speech directed at Australian citizens arguing either for or against keeping Queen Elizabeth as their monarch.

1 Work with a partner to research the idea of the British Commonwealth, considering why some Australians would like to vote to become completely independent.

2 Use your research to create a plan for your speech. Complete a copy of the table below, listing the reasons for and against Queen Elizabeth being Australia's monarch.

Queen Elizabeth II should no longer be the constitutional monarch of Australia, so that Australia is no longer governed by her as Head of the Commonwealth	
FOR	**AGAINST**

3 Write a draft of your speech. You should aim to use as many argumentative techniques as you can, including a range of rhetorical devices. For example, you could express strong opinions as though they are facts:

Queen Elizabeth is the best ambassador for Commonwealth countries. Having her as the head of the Commonwealth means that, in this world of chaos and war, Australia and England are bonded in peace and harmony.

Drama techniques: choreography

In scene 11, Colin travels into central London on the Underground. The action is described as an 'organic mass'.

1 Work as a class to re-enact this moment, considering how it could be performed or choreographed on stage. Choose one person to take the role of Colin and one or two people to direct and choreograph the movement. Practise and prepare the scene. Focus on how the staging can show how intimidating and threatening life in London must seem to Colin.

2 Think about how this moment could be staged in a real theatre production, for example:

- What costumes would you choose? How would you make Colin stand out?
- Would you use music or sound effects to support the drama or would you want the scene to be silent?

Writing to argue, persuade and advise

In scene 11, Colin decides to write a letter to the Queen to ask for her help to make Luke better.

1 Plan what Colin might say in his letter to the Queen to persuade her to help Luke. Use a fishbone organiser like the one below to help you plan your ideas. Add between four and six lines of argument, explaining what the Queen could do, and why, as well as why this would make a difference.

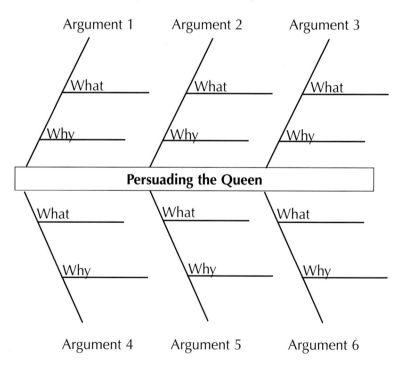

2 Make a list of five or six argumentative or persuasive features that you could use in your letter. For example:
- writing opinion as though it is fact
- using rhetorical questions
- using triple phrases.

You should also think about how your paragraphs link together.

3 When you have completed your plan, write your letter. Remember to use Colin's factual style and tone when writing, and you could also use some Australian dialect.

Active reading strategies: explaining characters' viewpoints

In order to explore the viewpoints of different characters, look again at the incident in scene 16, in which Alistair and Colin are returned home by the police. You are going to explore what Iris would say to Colin's mum and what Colin himself would say to her.

1 Draw two thought bubbles, one for Iris and one for Colin. In each bubble, jot down that character's account of the events, considering their views and their thoughts.

2 Add notes on their feelings about the situation and what they would say to Colin's mum when explaining it to her.

3 Write a short dramatic monologue in the form of a phone conversation. You only need to write Iris and Colin's sides of the conversation, as we don't hear his mum's responses on stage. Remember to use an informal style and include incomplete sentence fragments, to suggest that Colin's mum is interrupting. Make sure you write in the style that the character uses when speaking. You may find the following opening lines helpful as a starting point.

AUNTIE IRIS   Look, before you say a word, let me just say I did everything I could to make sure your boy didn't get into trouble...

COLIN   Look, mum, I know you're gonna go mad, but if you'd just let me tell me my side before you say anything...

Active reading strategies: considering characters' viewpoints

In scene 18, Colin tries to persuade the doctor to come to Australia to help his brother. When Colin says that Luke could die, the doctor is a little harsh, saying: 'Everyone here has got cancer! They could all die!!' When faced with people presenting an argument, it is helpful to argue back in a more logical and reasonable way, explaining your own views and using evidence to justify and support them. When you have to make a difficult point, it is important to be reasonable and positive, yet assertive, not giving in to people who make demands that we cannot meet.

1 Work with a partner to reread scene 18. Identify the arguments that Colin makes about why the doctor should fly to Australia to help Luke. Think of some further arguments that Colin could have used to persuade the doctor.

2 Construct a dialogue for a more effective argument between Colin and the doctor. Try to use language that will help the characters to understand each other's arguments better. The characters should give evidence, reasons and examples to help support their views and to challenge each other's arguments. Remember that the doctor should be sympathetic and positive towards Colin.

3 When you have written your dialogue, perform it with your partner. Then compare your lines of argument with those of another pair.

Drama techniques: inner thoughts

To build up an understanding of how relationships are established between two characters, you can freeze the action between lines of dialogue and have someone voice each character's thoughts about the other.

1 Reread scene 19, in which Colin and Ted meet for the first time.

2 Work as a group of four to act out this scene. Choose two people to play Colin and Ted, speaking their lines as they are written in the script. The other two of you should also take the roles of Colin and Ted, but you will voice their inner thoughts.

3 Act out the scene, but after each line of dialogue freeze the action and voice the inner thoughts of the person who has just spoken. You could use this example to start you off.

Colin   You OK?

All freeze, except for the person voicing Colin's thoughts.

Colin 2   I wonder what's wrong with him? I don't really want to ask – it seems private, but it'd be rude not to say anything at all!

Ted   No.

All freeze, except for the person voicing Colin's thoughts.

Ted   This kid must be mad – course I'm not OK! But at least he's asking. Everyone else just keeps walking away from me, like I'm diseased! It's not a disease, you know, it's just a man crying!

Active reading strategies: reading between the lines

As the relationship between Ted and Colin develops, their views about each other change and develop. Look back at scenes 20, 23 and 25 to consider the way Colin and Ted think about each other.

1 Work individually to trace the two characters' developing views of each other. Draw two speech bubbles, one for Ted and one for Colin. Divide each speech bubble into three sections, to represent the three scenes, as shown in the example below.

2 Write statements about how Colin and Ted felt about each
   other at each point in the play. Use temporal connectives,
   such as at *first, then* and *now*, to show how their feelings have
   changed or developed. Make sure you add a range of feelings.
   You may also wish to refer to examples from the text.

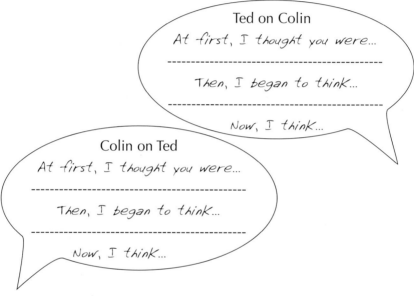

Drama techniques: dramatic monologue

When Griff dies, Colin is one of the only friends that Ted has, and
when Ted asks Colin to 'stay with me a while' after Griff dies, we
see that Ted has come to rely on Colin for support.

1 Create a dramatic monologue to explore Ted's thoughts and
   feelings towards Colin. Write as though you are Ted and
   summarise what Colin has meant to you, for instance, the way
   he has always allowed you to see the humour in the most
   serious of situations.

2 You may also wish to explain how you feel your friendship,
   although brief, is an incredibly strong one. You can also
   explore your hopes and predictions about Colin in the future,
   such as how he will cope following Luke's death.

Writing to imagine, explore and entertain

In scene 34, Colin is reunited with his family. The play finishes at this point, although there are many things that are left unresolved or incomplete. You are going to write an additional scene that explores Colin's motivation for returning to Australia.

1 Work in a small group to script a short scene showing what happens when Colin returns to Australia. You could show a reconciliation between Colin and Luke or a discussion between Colin and his parents about sending him to England, for example. In the scene, Colin should express his feelings about being sent away and explain why he decided to return.

2 Perform your scripted scene to another group and ask them for feedback, so that you can see whether they have understood Colin's motivation for returning to Australia.

After you have studied the play

Drama techniques: freeze frame

1 Working in a group of five or six, discuss what you think are the three most significant events in the play.

2 For each event, select the moment in the scene that you want to freeze frame in order to explore it in more detail.

3 Prepare your three freeze frames. Consider how you will move from one freeze frame to the next.

4 Perform your sequence of freeze frames for the rest of the class. Ask the class if they know which three events you were representing. If they are not able to guess what the scenes were, ask for feedback about how you could improve your freeze frames.

5 When all the freeze frames have been performed, discuss the events that you selected. Were some more common than others? Explore why these scenes stood out more than the rest for you.

Activities

Layers of meaning: play title

1 Consider the title, *Two Weeks with the Queen*. Think about what the original author, Morris Gleitzman, wanted the reader to think the title meant. What did he want the reader to think it meant before reading his novel? What new meanings might he have intended the reader to make by the end?

2 Draw a speech bubble like the one below. Write as if you are Morris Gleitzman and explain what you wanted the reader to think at the beginning, and why, and then what you wanted the reader to think by the end, and why. You may be able to think of more than one thing that Morris Gletizman might have wanted us to think.

> At the beginning, I wanted you to think that the title meant... because...
>
> By the end, I wanted you to think the title could also mean... because...

Wider reading

Morris Gleitzman has written many novels for teenagers, including *Toad Rage* and *Boy Overboard*. When you have finished studying *Two Weeks with the Queen*, you might want to read one of the novels and compare it with *Two Weeks with the Queen*.

1 Make a list of the similarities and differences between the two stories, including the following aspects.

Narrative viewpoint	Main character	Families
Who is telling the story? What similarities are there between the two texts?	What similarities and differences are there between the main characters?	What similarities and differences are there between the families?

102

Tone	Themes	Issues
What similarities and differences are there in the narrative voices that the writers use?	What are the two texts about and what similarities and differences are there between them?	What are the main problems in the two texts and how do these compare?
Written style	**Your response**	**Audience**
What similarities and differences are there between the way the two texts are written?	Which did you prefer, and why?	Who do you think would enjoy each of the stories? What similarities and differences are there between the intended audiences of the two texts?

Writing to analyse, review and comment

Following your comparison of the two texts, you are going to write a short analysis commenting on them and explaining what they do that is similar and what they do differently.

1 Your writing should provide a balanced analysis, so you will need to make sure you use paragraphs that connect the two analyses with connectives of comparison and contrast. Before you start writing, make a list of comparative and contrasting connectives, for example similarly and on the other hand. Try to make sure you have at least five or six different connectives for comparing and five or six for contrasting, so that you can use these to help you structure your writing.

2 Write your analysis. Make sure you use the appropriate connectives to help you structure your writing and that you also use evidence from the two texts. It would be particularly helpful if you revisit your notes from the previous activity and add details of examples from the text that support your view.

Reading for pleasure

If you enjoyed reading the play *Two Weeks with the Queen*, why not try...

Two Weeks with the Queen by Morris Gleitzman

Mary Morris's play is based on this fantastic novel. Like the play, the novel is both hilariously funny and poignant in telling the story of Colin and his family. Reading the novel gives you an excellent opportunity to explore the differences between plays and novels and the different techniques that authors use to tell a story.

ISBN 978 1 4058 3415 5

Boy Overboard by Morris Gleitzman

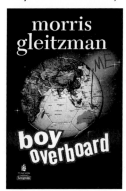

Jamal loves playing football, which isn't easy if your goalie has only one leg and you keep having to dodge landmines to get your ball back. When it is discovered that Jamal's mother has been secretly running a school, the family must leave their home in Afghanistan immediately and begin a long and dangerous journey to Australia.

ISBN 978 1 4058 1554 3

Once by Morris Gleitzman

Felix can't stop wondering what has happened to his parents. He's been living in an orphanage in the mountains for over three years now, and they still haven't come to get him. When men arrive one day and start burning books, Felix can't understand what is happening. But this is Poland in 1942 and the men are Nazis, come to burn Jewish books. Fearing for his parents, Felix escapes and embarks on a dangerous mission across Nazi-occupied Poland.

ISBN 978 1 4058 4130 6

Freak the Mighty by Rodman Philbrick

Maxwell Kane is feared and bullied because of his slowness and enormous size. With his father in jail for murdering his mother, nobody expects much of him. Kevin, on the other hand, is smart, quirky and funny with an insatiable curiosity and a zest for life. But Kevin suffers from a rare condition, which means he has a bent spine and can't walk without crutches. Yet the combination of Kevin and Maxwell is formidable and together they become Freak the Mighty.

ISBN 978 1 4058 3462 9